THE UNDERCOVER GAME

BY

MICHAEL A. DUBAICH

ISBN: 978-0-936014-30-2

Most of the names found in this book have been changed in order to protect identities. Some parts of the narrative have also been fictionalized in varying degrees for entertainment purposes.

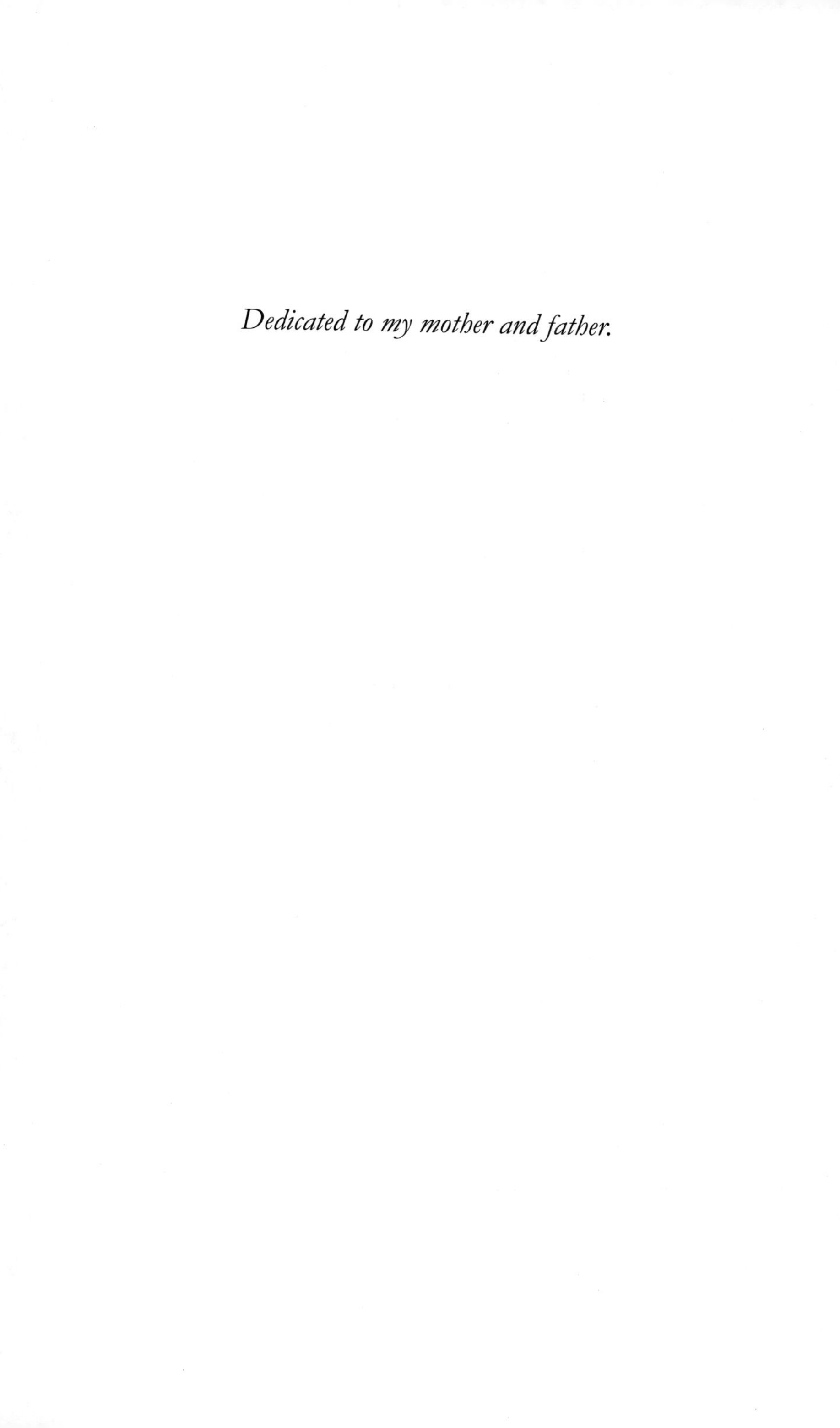

Dedicated to my mother and father.

CONTENTS

INTRODUCTION

The following stories are just a few of my experiences during my time as an undercover special agent for the Pennsylvania Game Commission. They took place sometime between 1990 and 1995 (I thought you should know that because some of the technology is old). The stories document the many challenges that covert investigators face, including the diverse and sometimes dangerous roles we assume while gathering evidence. Our focus is to bring to justice those who would profit by unlawfully taking and/or selling wildlife—wildlife which belongs to all of the citizens of the Commonwealth of Pennsylvania. Some of the names have been changed to protect identities.

I wore many hats working undercover. It is a lot like being an actor, except you only get one take, and your life may depend on you getting it right.

PART I

A SHEEP IN WOLF'S CLOTHING

"You gonna sleep all day, boy?"

My eyes struggle to open. In the darkness I can make out a dull light silhouetting a figure in the doorway. *Think, Mike.* My brain's trying to make sense of it all. *Where are you? Who are you? Damn. Drank too much. Not enough sleep. Too many towns, too many miles. C'mon, Mike, get your shit together. Who is this guy?*

The little guy in the part of my brain responsible for names, dates, and places is searching franticly, shuffling through stacks of papers. His computer is down.

Your fault, says the little guy. *You're the one who dumped beer all over my keyboard. I'm doing the best I can.* He grabs a crumbled piece of paper from the floor of my brain. *Aha! Got it.*

Suddenly, I remember. "Tom?" I groan. "What the fuck time is it?"

It's warm. No, hot. And I am in a trailer. First the smell of bacon frying. Then the sound, far off, like snow on a power line.

"It's time for you to get your ass out of bed," Tom barks. "We got deer to kill."

My bladder feels like it can only feel when you drank too much and decided that sleeping was more important than taking time for one last piss. I roll off the bed as Tom clicks on the light. A bare bulb hangs on wires falling out of the smoke-stained ceiling. Very cosmopolitan. Christ, it looks like some giant picked this place up and shook it like a snow globe. Only, instead of sparkles of white, what's floating to the ground in here is empty beer cans, old newspapers, clothes, and dirt.

The trailer's only door is always open. At least in the winter. Tom has the good fortune to have a couple of gas wells on his property, so he has all the gas he can use, free of charge.

"What?" Tom chuckles, as I put on my boots. "Don't you like how the cleaning lady does my bathroom?"

I am a big man. Almost six-four, two-twenty. Tom is bigger. He has me by two inches and sixty or seventy pounds. I remember first time we shook hands, his bear paws almost swallowed mine.

I stumble out the front door. Not that I have to. One

of the finer amenities of Uncle Tom's Trailer is indoor plumbing. The little guy in the part of my brain in charge of memory performs another miracle. His computer is running again. It's December in northwest Pennsylvania. It should be cold outside. My brain keeps the information coming. The frosty air will help clear my head.

The little guy upstairs is right, as always. It's cold outside. The steam rising from my urine, a final affirmation. It carries my thoughts into the night sky, like incense burning in a church. God help me.

Tom is a poacher. He knows it. I know it. I am an undercover game warden. I know it. I pray he doesn't.

It's been said that being a game warden is the most dangerous job in America. And there are statistics to back it up. You gotta be half crazy to be out in the woods, mostly alone, when everyone you confront has a gun or guns. And if you gotta be half crazy to be a game warden, then, by god, the handful of officers who have ever made their living as undercover wardens went the extra mile and deserve to be considered clinically insane.

The illegal commercial trade in wildlife is second only to drugs in revenue, and nobody really gives two shits. I hear people say, "It's a victimless crime. Nobody really gets hurt." On that I call BULL SHIT. The "nobody" who gets hurt are the 12.7 million citizens of Pennsylvania. In the Constitution of Pennsylvania, Article I, Section 27 reads:

> **NATURAL RESOURCES AND THE PUBLIC ESTATE.**
>
> The people have a right to clean air, pure water, and to the preservation of the natural, scenic, historic and esthetic values of the environment. Pennsylvania's public natural resources are the common property of all the people, including generations yet to come. As trustee of these resources, the Commonwealth shall conserve and maintain them for the benefit of all the people.

Deer, in fact all wild animals, belong to every citizen of the Commonwealth of Pennsylvania. When they pinned a badge on me I took this oath:

> "I do solemnly swear that I will support, obey, and defend the Constitution of the United States, and the Constitution of this Commonwealth; and that I will discharge the duties of my office with fidelity."

I do not take this vow lightly.

Another refrain I often hear is, "I don't mind if they poach deer, as long as they are going to eat them." To me, that's like saying it's OK to rob the bank, as long as you are going to spend the money.

I can tell by the size of the fawn it's one that was born in the summer, not in May, like the majority. But deer are prolific breeders, and if the does are not bred in October or November, they will keep coming into heat until they conceive. Looking at this little bugger, it can't be more than four months outside its momma. I am hoping Tom doesn't see the young deer and its mother as the headlights of his truck slice through the predawn darkness at a perpendicular angle to the spotlight I'm holding out of the passenger window of his truck. But before I can move the light down, it hits the tapetum, which lines the retina of animals with developed night vision and reflects the light back into the eye where the brain can use the available light again to see in the dark. The light is also reflected back out through the wide open pupil, making the eyes appear to glow like the severed ends of fiber optic cables. It's this glow that catches Tom's eye, causing his brain to signal his left foot to hit the clutch and his right foot to hit the brake, bringing the truck to a lurching stop on the dirt country road.

"You fucking flat-lander," Tom growls. "If you

ain't gonna pay attention, you might as well stay home. Git that light back up there. I just saw a couple a deer."

Tom eases his large frame out of the driver's side of the truck, while simultaneously easing out his trusty thirty-aught-six with the choreographed moves and practiced skill of Baryshnikov. His eye finds the crosshairs and centers them between the doe's.

This particular doe is in her eighth winter. As deer go in Pennsylvania, where hunters shoot almost 60 percent of the deer each year, she is practically a dinosaur. She learned at an early age to avoid any contact with men. Once the leaves begin to turn, she never forages during the day. She eats all night when the smell of men in the woods is almost nonexistent. She seeks refuge where even other deer are seldom found. Because of her survival tactics, she is almost always bred late in the year. When most of the does are already pregnant, ensuring their fawns are born in May or June when the food supplies are most abundant, she is hiding, cautious. Whether a conscious part of her survival strategy or not, by waiting she would most likely be impregnated by another deer who knew how to survive.

Back in the 1990's, the chances of a buck living through the fall hunting seasons in Pennsylvania were just about one in ten. Those that lived would be the kind of buck whose genetics this doe would want to pass on to her offspring. The problem is, her fawns were born in July or August when the summer heat had begun to suck the life out of the succulent vegetation. It also means her fawns are facing the harsh winter two months younger and smaller than other fawns. There is a price to pay for every survival strategy. She is past her breeding prime, and for the first time since her first year, she only gave birth to one fawn. The little buck is curious but smart. His dam and sire are both survivors, and he too has a good chance to carry her genes to another generation.

At least before we spotted them.

The doe is dead before she hits the ground. The young fawn is startled but still stands next to mom. If she isn't running, it must be OK. The flash of fire and roaring noise from behind the blinding light makes it want to take flight, but if it stays near mom everything will be fine.

Tom howls with laughter and spits. "Now that's how it's done, asshole! Hold that light back up. I think the other one is still there."

"That one's too small, Tom," I say. "It ain't worth ten dollars. Let it go. There ain't enough meat on its bones to bother skinnin' it."

Tom backs up his truck so the headlights shine on the deer.

"I'll go up and get her, Tom,. You wait with the truck in case someone comes along."

"That little fucker is still standin' there, Mike. Here," he says, handing me the rifle, "you might as well take him."

The hardest part about this job is trying not to do what you are being paid to arrest the bad guys for doing. It wouldn't look good in court if you broke as many laws as the suspected violator. The problem is you can't act like Mr. Clean. When you run with assholes, you are expected to be an asshole. One of the final tests you are often called upon to pass is the Shoot The Deer At Night Test. Hell, if old Mike here shoots a deer at night, he can't be a game warden.

Tom glares at me and spits through his tobacco-stained teeth, offering me the rifle.

It is now 4 a.m. and I'm not even sure what county we're in, let alone what township. All I have on me is a knife, and no one but Tom and God knows where I am. The dispatchers who handle calls to the Game Commission and are the uniformed game warden's lifeline have a saying, "You may know where you are, and God may know where you are, but if the dispatcher doesn't know where you are, only God can help you." *The dispatchers aren't even supposed to know I exist.*

"Hell, Tom," I say, "it ain't worth wasting a bullet over. Besides we don't need to draw more attention to ourselves by shootin' that little pecker. Let's hurry up and grab the big one and get the fuck out of here."

Tom isn't used to being talked back to. But that's why he likes me. He figures if I'm not afraid of him, I'm not afraid of anything. I don't have his complete trust yet, but I do have his respect.

He shoves the rifle back into the truck and says, "Well, stop standin' there like a cigar-store Indian. Get your ass up there and drag her down here. Don't bother to take time to gut her, either. We need to keep movin'. Besides, some dumb shit game warden might be smart enough to spot the gut pile, and he'll know we've been here. Get movin,' boy."

I've managed to work my way out of shooting this deer, but the chance will come again and I will have to come up with another excuse. But I can work on that later. Right now I want to get that doe in the truck. More importantly, I want to get back on the same side of the truck headlights as Tom. It's still just 4 a.m., after all, and only God can help me.

Tom is behind those headlights with a rifle, and he may not have liked the fact that I refused to shoot the fawn. If he wants to take me out, here is his best chance. My mind flashes back to the big doe dropping where she stood from the impact of Tom's bullet. He might have to give me a dose of the same medicine.

As I approach the doe, the little buck holds his ground, standing next to his mother's lifeless body. Unbeknownst to me, at that same time, Tom is easing the thirty-aught-six out over the hood of his truck. I can't see any of this because, like the deer, I am blinded by the truck's headlights. The difference is, while the deer may not have had the mental capacity to know what was behind the blinding light, I sure as heck do. *Who is smarter now, Mike, you or the deer?* Here I have intentionally positioned myself in the same situation the dead deer faced only seconds earlier. "Real fucking bright, dip-shit," I murmur in the chill darkness.

The thirty-aught-six is not every night poacher's weapon of choice. Most prefer smaller caliber rifles, like a twenty-two, since they make less noise and are not as expensive as the larger calibers. And if the warden is after you, it's a hell of lot easier on the wallet to throw an old twenty-two out the window than your prized hunting rifle.

A bullet fired from a thirty-aught-six can travel up to six miles. It can easily pass through a half-inch steel plate and keep on killing on the other side. I have seen exit wounds in deer carcasses bigger than my fist. On many occasions I have seen the way it will disintegrate the deer's skull. And that's just what I am looking at now. The top of the doe's head, from the eyeballs on up, is completely gone. A mass of splintered bone and exploded gray matter is all that remains to generate the steam that is rising into the starry sky, carrying the deer's last thoughts into the heavens.

All of this rushes through my mind as, unbeknownst to me, the muzzle of Tom's thirty-aught-six crosses my body and he pushes off the safety. Light travels at 360,000 miles per second; sound, a mere 1,100 feet per second; a bullet from a thirty-aught-six, 2,500 feet per second. I have always been good at physics, but you don't have to be Albert Einstein to know that you would see the flash of the gunpowder exploding from the end of the barrel before you heard the noise or felt the bullet smash into your body.

Incredibly, as I approach the carcass the little buck stubbornly stands there. He looks at me curiously as I bend to grasp a leg of the doe. Then he steps towards me and stretches his neck to nuzzle my hand. I speak softly to him, assuring him I will make the bastard who had taken his mother pay for his crimes. I can see the little pedicles on his skull, which one day will grow into a massive set of antlers.

I turn towards Tom's truck to see if he is observing any of this odd behavior on behalf of the young wild buck. At the same time, my right hand reaches out to scratch the top of the young buck's head and rub the pedicles, as if I need some sort of tangible evidence to confirm this surreal scene. As my eyes try to search behind the blinding headlights, I see the fire fly from what can only be the barrel of Tom's thirty-aught-six. The same rifle that only a moment ago vaporized the doe's brain.

A flicker of brilliant light erupts from the blackness behind the headlights, causing my hand to flinch and bump the fawn's head down just as the bullet arrives milliseconds after. The little buck has had enough. So have I. As he scrambles away I swear I can see the perfectly round hole the bullet makes as its passes through his right ear. I am a little afraid and a lot angry.

As I approach the truck, Tom is still laughing whole heartedly as he turns away, just long enough to spring the latch holding the tail gate. Turning back to face me, he starts to say, "Son, you should have seen the look on your pie hole when I sh—"

That's when I hit him with everything I had. For the readers who have never punched anyone in the head, Hollywood seldom gets it right. The best way I can describe it, it's like punching a twelve-pound bowling ball wrapped in a towel. It works, but it hurts.

"You mother-fucking cock-sucking asshole!" I scream. "You think that was funny, you stupid fuck?"

Tom actually takes two steps back and drops his ass onto to the opened tail gate. He shakes his head to try and clear the cobwebs.

Wiping his sleeve across his nose and mouth, he looks at the little bit of blood on his arm and says, "Well, I guess I had that comin'."

///////////////////////////////

Peter Thomas "Petey" Rossi is an affable man of Italian decent. He operates a restaurant in the local mall called Pizza Romo, which is owned by his father, who is rumored to be connected with the Vegas Mafia. His gregarious nature and accent is half Italian and three quarters coal-cracker, making him the perfect pitch-man as he promotes his pizza pies, Stromboli, and calzones.

What brought Woj and me to Rossi's door is case number NE91-13. This soon-to-be-extensive file begins with a Request for Special Investigations form submitted by Wildlife Conservation Officer Fred Merluzzi. Merluzzi has information from numerous reliable sources that one Peter Rossi is purchasing deer from local poachers and using it in place of or to supplement the beef and pork he uses at his restaurant. Officer Merluzzi's narrative goes on to evince that Rossi deals in automatic weapons and other firearms. Mike and I come to agree he isn't using or selling venison in his restaurant menu, but the remainder of the intelligence the local officer provides is spot on.

I have many partners in my term as an undercover game warden, and Mike Wojtecki is the one I work with on this case. A Vietnam vet, he is as American as Apple Computer and resolute with his opinions. His friends, of which I was one, call him "Woj" (pronounced with a long "oh" sound). He and I spend a lot of time on the road together over the years, and we learn we can trust and rely on each other, especially when the dung smacks the rotating blades, so to speak.

As the investigation begins to unfold, Rossi informs us that he can get us anything we want—sporting arms, audio/video equipment, automatic weapons, four wheelers, anything, he says, except booze and drugs. Rossi doesn't use either one and prefers not to buy or sell them. He has no such prohibitions, however, when it comes to buying and selling stolen property. Rossi is what you call a "fence." For those unfamiliar with the jargon of street hoods, a "fence" is someone who buys stolen property at a significantly reduced price and then resells it at the current stolen property rate, usually about 60-percent retail. Rossi loves to hunt and kill. Consequently, he has little love for the Pennsylvania Game Commission (PGC)

One of the most arduous parts of initiating an investigation is figuring out how to contact the subjects in a manner that makes them believe you are who you say you are. When we first read the Request for Special Investigation for Rossi, we both wonder how in the hell we are going to get in good with this guy. He doesn't drink or frequent bars. He doesn't have a pool table or a dart board. We can't think of a way to approach him, so we decide to let him approach us. We could at least hang around and see what we can hear.

We stop in every once in a while and split a pitcher of Yuengling and a pizza. Rossi is a hustler. He knows everybody, and it sounds like he had a lot of deals in the making. Turns out we hear a lot about guns, including some automatic rifles, and hunting. So, Woj and I always wear camouflage clothing and talk loudly about hunting stories that exist only in our minds.

As we are walking out one day, from behind the counter Rossi raises his voice and says, "You guys like to hunt?"

"No," I reply. "This color clothing just matches our eyes."

This obviously confuses Rossi. "Your eyes? What the hell do your eyes have to do…" Then his face brightens.

"OK. I get it. You're a funny guy, you know that?"

"Funny looking, maybe," Woj retorts with a tip of his hat.

With the formalities over, we walk over to the counter in front of Rossi and talk about the things hunters talk about.

"Let me show you some pictures of a buck I just got with my bow," Rossi states proudly, while producing a set of photos showing the head and neck of a nice, white-tailed buck, including the compound bow and arrows he supposedly used to kill it.

"Bow and arrow?" says Woj, examining the pictures. "Like hell. I can still see the tire tracks on this one."

Rossi, looking stunned, cries back, "There ain't no tire tracks on that deer."

I try to calm him down. "He's just fuckin' with you, man. Mike here thinks that just because he hunts with his truck bumper, everybody does."

Rossi grumbles while collecting his pictures. "Well, that ain't no roadkill."

Later, as we are walking across the mall parking lot toward my pickup truck, I shake my head and say, "Christ on a crutch, Woj! You damn near fucked that one up."

"Why? What did I do wrong?"

"What did you do wrong? That fucking buck was a fucking roadkill. Do you not remember the officer telling us he had just received information that Rossi picked up a nice, road-killed buck and put his tag on it so he could brag about it?"

"Oh, yeah. Sorry about that," replies Woj. "I was only

kidding with him."

"In this job it doesn't matter what you think," I tell him. "The only thing that matters when you work undercover is what they think. Remember: words not spoken need not be taken back, words once spoken never can be."

//////////////////////////////

When the gun roars, I flinch, turn toward my partner and smile. I smile because my partner and I are still alive. The rabbit keeps on running after Rossi's miss. Woj, whose wit will one day be legend, says,"Christ, Petey, you couldn't hit a bull in the ass with a board!"

"You're giving him too much credit," I add. "I don't think he can hit the fucking ground he's standing on.

Rossi, looking as if he's trying to figure out what Einstein had in mind when he developed his theory of relativity, breaks into a broad grin and replies in his brilliant way, "Fuck you both!"

After failing to hit the cottontail Rossi, Woj, and I continue to fight our way through the weed-choked terrain. Rossi is just above and to my left; Woj is off to my right. I pause beside what is left of an old, broken-down ATV in the field we are hunting and pretend to have more than a mild interest in the dilapidated machine. As I stand considering the quad, Rossi's ears are still ringing from the twelve-gauge blast that did little more than educate the cottontail.

"Hey, Mikey, you want to buy a four-wheeler? I have one for sale right now for a good price, but it's hot."

I don't even so much as flinch at the word "hot" and reply, "It depends on how big and how much."

"It's a brand new Husky 500, four-wheel drive, loaded. I'll sell it to you for a grand, but it's hot."

Once again I act like I didn't even hear the word "hot."

Rossi is becoming frustrated with my apparent lack of understanding of crime slang. "When I say hot," he says, "I mean it's stolen."

Jesus, the jury is going to love this guy, I think, as I quickly glance at Woj, who is grinning that grin only two men who trust each other with their lives and the lives of their families can fully understand. Then I reply, "Yeah, I know what it means, Petey. I'm Irish, not Italian."

After Rossi's patented "Fuck you!" we continue on through the field.

Moments like this are hallmark moments. Obviously, while living the life of a law violator, you cannot just whip out your note pad and pen to record the day, date, and time of every event that could provide crucial evidence months or years later, when you are called upon to present your case in court. For the most part, you need to have a good memory. The brain is like a muscle in that exercise, and practice can make it stronger. I was always impressed with the servers who could take food and beverage orders from any number of people and return their requests with flawless ease, sans instrument, device, or contrivance. It is only a matter of hard work and practice. This is the first time Rossi has offered, and demonstrated, knowledge of receiving, possessing, and selling stolen property as the intelligence provided by the local uniformed officers indicated. Knowing and recalling the day, date, time, location, and circumstances of this epiphany will help substantiate and strengthen our case.

We work our way up toward some trees and start up a brushy draw. I am just now putting the little guy in my head to work on storing that information, when the brush explodes in front of me. I can feel the burst of displaced air molecules strike my face, forcing my eyes to close. And then the deafening—BOOM!

At the sound of the first blast of the shotgun, I can feel the wind rushing past my ears as a few flecks of grass, weeds, seeds, and dirt flurry around me. That turkey was close, so close I almost stomp on her as I bully my way through the choking, thorny bramble. I'm not sure if it is the tips of her tail feathers or the jet wash of her powerful wing beats that I feel on my cheeks as the hen breaks from cover. A female wild turkey can weigh was much as twelve pounds, and they can displace a large volume of air and scatter some brush, trying to get that mass moving hurriedly.

I swing the barrel of my worn Ithaca twelve-gauge pump-action and my vision to my left. Seeing and hearing, "BOOM!...BOOM!...BOOM!" Then,"MOTHER... FUCKER!" Rossi has missed again.

Our hunt finally ended, we all climb into Rossi's Ford Bronco and head back to his house. As we pull into his driveway and exit the vehicle, Rossi turns to us. "Hey Mike and Mike," he says, "come here and follow me. I want to show you guys what I got."

We follow him to an old corncrib in back of a field behind his beautiful, newly constructed house/mansion.

"The pizza business must be pretty good," Woj murmurs as we trail behind Rossi.

"Pretty fucking profitable," I reply. "I wonder how many Stromboli you gotta sell to afford one of these."

Wojtecki's face breaks into a smile. "Hey, Petey!" he yells. "How many—"

But then he stops mid-sentence as I walk by him and give his camouflaged jacket a sharp tug, quietly growling, "Now's not the time, Mike."

Woj has a rapier wit. He doesn't always know when it's proper to display it, though. This is not the first time Woj used questionable timing in the delivery of his punchline.

Mike Wojtecki is ten years my senior, but he never holds it against me. By the time he graduates from our officer training academy and joins the Special Investigations Unit (SIU), I already have three years in uniform and another three years undercover. My record speaks for itself, and he is never too proud to ask for advice or accept criticism. He knows I like to have some fun, but he also knows I take my job as seriously as a serial killer takes his second victim.

Woj has backbone. He did some hard time in Nam, not that he ever talks about it. He never offers, and I never ask. He did show me a couple of photographs that to this day my mind's eye can clearly detail. I also witnessed him emasculate some arrogant blowhard one time, when he seethed, "You pogey bait motherfucker! You spent all of your time in-country, on a mother fuckin', linoleum fuckin' floor! So shut your fuckin' pie hole!"

//////////////////////////////

As we approach the old corncrib in the field behind Rossi's home, we can see a blue tarp with an obvious large lump in the middle. Rossi walks over to the tarp, pulls it back, and reveals a red, three-wheeled ATV, otherwise known as a "trike," that's in pretty good condition.

"Hey, Petey," I say, "I hate to question your math skills, but back in that field you told me you had a *four*-wheeler for sale. Now, let me see…" I begin pointing my finger at each tire, "…we have one, two, three wheels and—"

Rossi cuts me off. "Fuck you guys. I just wanted to show you what else I had. The good one is in the garage."

"Well," says Woj, "let's go see it then."

Before walking away, I go over and squat close to the right side of the trike, looking closely while using my thumb to rub off some of the dust and grime.

"What are you doing?" Rossi yells out to me. "I thought we were going to look at the big one?"

Woj looks at Rossi and, grabbing his crotch, says, "I got a big one you can look at."

What I am doing is looking for a serial number or identification number. It would most likely be located on the side of the frame or engine block. It could be stamped into the metal itself or on a metal plate attached to the frame or engine block. The Commonwealth is not likely to lend Woj and me the several hundred dollars it will take to buy these ATVs unless we're pretty sure they're stolen. The best way to do that is to compare the serial number of the ATV in question to a list of reported stolen ones. These serial numbers are always long, fifteen to twenty characters, and this one is no exception. *Christ*, I think, *I am never going to get this.*

"I'm just checking to make sure it's in good shape!" I yell back to Rossi. "Just wanna make sure you're not trying to fuck me." I am stalling. My eyes are focused on that line of numbers, trying to picture them in my mind. When I think I have them remembered, I jump up and say, "Let's go and see what else we have."

Rossi lets us in through the man-door on the side of the four-car garage. Then he points to the big, dark-green Husky 500, four-wheel drive. "Now, that's a nice one," he says. "But you can't ride it anywhere around here. This thing is smokin' hot."

"We gotta think about this one," I reply. "What do you want for the trike?"

"I'll take three-hundred."

"Will you take two?"

Rossi takes a moment and then replies, "How about two fifty?"

"So, two-hundred?"

"C'mon, Mike, old buddy. Give me two fifty."

"Two-hundred is all I've got on me," I say. "I'll go one fifty."

"What? Now you're going the wrong way." Rossi lets

out a sigh. "OK, all right," he says, "two-hundred it is."

"Thank you," I say, reaching out to shake his hand. "We're going to need to take the cap off the truck so we can get the trike in the bed. We'll come back tomorrow."

Mike and I head back to our "bat cave" to catch up on some paperwork and set up for the next day. In order to get to Special Investigation headquarters, aka "The Island," one has to travel through a locked gate across a single-lane concrete bridge approximately 150 yards long, thirty feet above the river, with no guard rails, and onto an island in a wildlife propagation area that prohibits anyone from entering except authorized personnel. The game commission purchased the 40' x 100' metal building and the land surrounding it from a sand-and-gravel company previously housed there. The building's interior was converted to contain two bedrooms, two, offices, two bathrooms, a kitchen, and plenty of room for parking or repairing vehicles. Previously, the Bureau of Land management used it as a game lands crew headquarters.

It's from this building that I call the boss to give him the serial number from the trike, or at least what I am able to remember of it. At this point the serial number is of no consequence, since we are going to bring it to SIU headquarters anyway.

//////////////////////////////

"Come on, Ray!" squeals Gina. "Shoot that fucker! Shoot that fucker! Shoot that fucker!" The probing beam from the spotlight she is holding just outside of the window of Raymond Gibson's pickup truck illuminates the bucolic surroundings including a prime, eight-point buck. Just like the doe on my jacklighting night with Tom, this male deer stands transfixed by the effulgence.

"Shut the fuck up, Gina," Raymond hisses. "You're gonna spook him."

The heavy-antlered buck is blinded, so he just keeps on standing there while Raymond, with rehearsed, consummate skill, ends the trophy deer's days with one precisely placed round to the head. And with that shot, Raymond also ends the hopes of many an honest, law-abiding wildlife enthusiast who would love to have encountered such a magnificent creature. With that shot he ends the dreams of any sportsman or sportswomen imagining that same weighty set of antlers affixed to a hunter's den or a hunting camp's wall. Lawful hunters wouldn't think of cheating by blinding the animal first.

Woj and I are standing astounded in the driveway of Rossi's palatial home as the petite young woman recounts her and her man Raymond's wonderful night of poaching. She is obstreperous, prancing about giggling and howling as she recaps every detail of their excellent adventure, using language that makes us two game wardens blush.

The provincial Raymond and urbane Gina are the newest additions to our growing list of violators in action. The couple steals three deer from the citizens of Pennsylvania that November evening. Gibson's rundown, beaten up, broke down, mostly black Toyota pickup can't haul the deer, however, so the enterprising young man stashes the three carcasses.

I offer to take him in my truck to pick them up. "Woj can stay here and entertain Rossi and Gina and with his fart tricks."

With me behind the wheel, Gibson directs us to the spot. "Pull over right before that bridge," he says. "They're right down over this bank."

Once we locate the deer, we both grab a set of legs and start toward the rear of my truck. I am just about to swing the head of the deer up onto to the open tailgate, when I hear a vehicle coming. We are parked on the back side of a 120-degree bend, so while we can hear the vehicles approaching, we can't see them until they're right up on us.

"Car coming, Ray!" I call out. There really is nothing you can do about it. You can only hope that it isn't trouble.

When Gibson sees the truck coming around the bend, he drops his half of the deer and dives into the bushes. After the vehicle passes, Ray barely has his hands back on his deer when a pickup comes from the opposite direction, and he again scrambles for cover.

"Ray, what the fuck are you doing?" I ask. "For Christ's sake, act like there is nothing going on here. When they see you running away, they're going to wonder what you're running from. Besides, you're wasting time. We should have been out of here already. The longer we sit here, the better chance we have of getting busted."

Minutes later we pull into Rossi's driveway, and, luckily, it doesn't look like Wojtecki has insulted or killed anybody. I hop out of my truck and make for the trailer hitch, where I open the first the rear window of my truck cap and then drop the tail gate. While the other four persons are examining the buck and two does, I analyze the tarp cam, and my analysis reveals what I had feared. While hurrying to get the deer into my truck, I had allowed my excitement to make me careless. I had pushed the eight-point buck too far forward, and his antlers, which had been responsible for his death, are now trying to bring about mine. They have become entangled in the blue tarp, exposing the back of the camera as well as the two—one for power, one for video—black, shielded wires.

Thinking quickly, I mumble something about the blood oozing from the buck's nose and how it's dripping off of the tarp. Then, vaulting into the truck bed, I try to place as much of myself between the exposed camera and Rossi as possible. "Trying to the keep the damn blood from getting all over the floor of my bed," I explain while I tug at the tarp and fuss with the deer. "Blood is a bitch to get off a truck bed, and I don't need anybody nosing around." I crawl further in and, while rearranging the buck's head, I am able to right the tarp cam without notice. Or so I think.

As I'm about to climb down from the back of the truck, Rossi scrambles forward on his hands and knees and says, "Wait a second. I wanna see something."

I watch in abject horror as he moves toward the camera. My blood pressure spikes and my face flushes as my adrenal glands pump full bore. I can hear Rossi telling reputed mobster Sal Pietre, "If these guys are game wardens, they are dead, dead."

Now everything is going in slow motion, except for my mind. I'm not sure what I'm going to do, but I'm sure as hell not gonna just stand there and watch helplessly.

I've been with the game commission for nine years by this point, and I'm already an unarmed defensive tactics instructor, a PR-24 Police baton instructor, a tactical handcuffing instructor, and a firearms instructor.

I've received tons of training from some highly skilled, extremely capable people. But where I really learned to brawl was as a twenty-one-year-old bouncer at the Esquire Lounge and Supper Club during a gas-and-oil boom in Dickinson, North Dakota.

Thoughts are racing through my brain. *What are you going to say, Mike? That it's just parts of a home surveillance kit you were messing with? That you were having trouble with things being stolen from the truck?* This case has taken years of our lives, hours and days of dedication, reams of paper, thousands of miles. We have a couple of good charges, but we have so much more to do yet. If Rossi flips out now, there is no way he is coming out of the back of this truck without my consent and control. And, no matter what, I am getting my partner safely home to his wife.

Rossi stops crawling and, leaning on his left arm, reaches out with his right hand straight to the no-longer-concealed camera. It seems to take forever. Then, seizing the antlers of the dead buck, he turns and looks at me hovering over him. "Just wanted to see if it was a seven- or eight-point."

After my heart stops racing and the white noise of fear mixed with adrenaline pumps out of my ear canals, I hand $150 to Raymond Gibson.

Accounting for monies expended to procure evidence is but one of the piles, reams, masses, heaps, hundreds, thousands, millions of mother-fuckin' forms, fact sheets, and because-I-said-so-reports we have to complete as part of our job. Our covert operations money comes in the form of checks issued to our real names. The thing is, the state government cannot issue checks to fictitious names, so covert accounts undergo the most thorough accounting in the state. I have a driver's license and Social Security numbers in three different names, from three different states. All of the major credit card companies have security departments that will issue MasterCard, Visa, and American Express. It wouldn't take much effort to extort money, especially if you fell on hard times or were just plain greedy. All of this fictitious information must be available and accessible to the government law enforcement agencies, while at the same time remaining inaccessible to criminals.

It might take three years to develop a cover, credit history, utility bills, and bank accounts, all while working under a different cover.

The advent of things like Google, Yahoo, People Finder, Facebook, etc., have made it even harder. If you claim to be somebody from somewhere, you better be able to show it.

You never know where you could face unexpected trouble. For example, this one time I was in a bank trying to set up a new checking account. I had a new Social Security number, which I had not too long before memorized, and the card to prove it. I confidently recited the number to the teller, and after she entered it into the system, she looked puzzled and asked if I wouldn't mind giving it to her again. When I did, she got the same result.

"Do you happen to have the card with you?"

"Yes," I replied, digging the card out of my wallet and handed it to her. She promptly headed for the manager, who by this point had hurried out of her office to have a look at me. The manager then tried her computer to see if it was user error.

"Is there some sort of a problem?" I asked.

"Yes," said the manager. "It's saying that this Social Security number was just issued."

I never missed a beat. "Oh, that," I said. "Yeah, they had to issue me a new number because my old one was stolen and compromised." According to Social Security, there is no way anyone from that bank or any other bank should be able to make a phone call and learn anything about that card number, other than whether it's valid or not. "That's why I came in here today," I continued. "I need to open new accounts, since I had to get new numbers."

The vast majority of the checks we need to cash are under $1,000. I can take them to my bank and cash them. The check I need to cash today, however, is for ten grand. I could deposit it in my bank, but I need the cash in two days, and my bank will not allow you to use any part of that money until that check clears—usually three days later. The account that holds the covert operating funds is a certain bank, and of course the checks that are used to draw on the funds are from that same bank. I determine the best chance I had to turn that paper into cash was at bank in that chain. It was still proving to be a pain in the ass.

I had specifically asked the people at Social Security about such a scenario, and emphatically they said the only information they were allowed to divulge was the current status of the card. It's paramount that you have a good Social Security number, since it is the foundation upon which your monetary history is constructed. You cannot get a checking account without one. If the number is not secure, the entire person you are trying to create will not live long.

These checking accounts are fueled by checks issued from a covert account with a major national bank, and at the time, they could only be issued and endorsed by the

Game Commission's Chief of Special Operations. These checks could be up to $500 for food, drinks, business cards, ball caps, etc.; up to $1,500 to establish and/or fund a covert business, pay informants, purchase evidence, etc.

Any amount over that can only be used to purchase evidence and may only be used on the case you listed on your official request for funding. That's why converting a check issued in your given name to the bank account listed in your covert name can, at times, be challenging.

////////////////////////////////

It's a gelid fall morning in northeast Pennsylvania when Woj and I return to Rossi's house. I don't mind seeing the thermometer on the low side. In fact I prefer it that way, particularly on this fine day, because today is the debut of "jacket cam."

The bulky camouflaged jacket I am wearing would look out of place on a warmer day. It keeps out the cold as advertised, but it also serves a dual purpose hiding the miniature camera body, equally minuscule camera lens, and the comparatively elephantine video recorder. The video recorder and accompanying battery are about the size of a brick and almost as heavy. We recorded the more significant interactions with subjects on 8mm video. This footage is invaluable in that it serves as a pictorial transcript as well as incontrovertible evidence of who, what, when, and how much. This is my first time using it on a real case, and I'm worried it isn't going to work or, worse yet, be discovered by someone.

As we turn into Rossi's driveway, I look over at Woj, yawning. "I hope this fucker's stolen," I say, reaching into the coat to flip the toggle switch and power up the newly installed camera. "Try not to pick your nose, and remember how we practiced. Keep the action in front of me and the camera."

"Don't you worry about my nose," Woj fires back. "If it ain't stolen, you just bought the state of Pennsylvania a nice three-wheeler."

"So that's how it's gonna be?" I say, grinning.

"What?"

"When *we* do something good, it's I or me or mine. But when *we* do something wrong, you always point your finger at me saying *he*, *him*, or *his*."

I pull our truck down by the corncrib where Rossi is waiting for us. The blue tarp is still there with the bump under it. It's covered with a sparkling, brilliant frost that crackles loudly as Woj and I each grab an end and pull it off of the trike.

Then, just as the tarp is settling back to the frozen

ground, I look up. "Someone is coming down the driveway," I say. "At least he started to. Now looks like he's heading toward us." A primer-gray sedan bounces its way through the old field, bringing two occupants to the corncrib where Rossi, Woj, and I are standing. "Who the fuck is that?" The dilapidated old four-door Ford swings away from us, stops, and with a loud clunk goes into reverse and creeps back toward us again. The driver isn't going slow on purpose, though. He has the gas pedal floored and that old, eight-cylinder 400 Ford is screaming, wheels spinning and thrusting mud, and rocks and frost-covered, dead golden rod back along the quarter panels, windshield, and doors. Thank God for posi-traction, I think as the car lurches backward to within ten feet of our little group.

"That's just Norm," says Rossi.

The door hinges protest loudly as the front doors on both sides are forced open. One passenger and the driver exit the mud-splattered, smoking wreck of a car. None of these characters believes in introductions, especially Rossi Woj and I learn the man who climbed from out behind the wheel is Norman Silver Jr.; his passenger is his son Norman Silver III. Neither of them mentions the ATV that's now completely exposed. They look like they've seen it before.

Silver Jr. is about five foot ten and slightly built, with

bedraggled, dirty blond hair down to his shoulders. He is wearing a scuffed, well worn, oil-stained, motorcycle jacket. It is his signature, statement message to the world that he is one badass, not-to-be-fucked-with hombre.

Anyone looking at Norman Silver III can tell he is his father's son. He is of similar height and build, and his hair is the identical color as Silver Jr.'s, maybe a little shorter. The only thing missing is the motorcycle jacket. "We got a couple for you," Junior announces, as he turns the key in the lock to pop the trunk lid.

Rossi looks at me and grins. "Nice deer, eh Mike?"

I step up to the middle of the trunk and look down at a brace of white-tailed deer, both adult females shot through the neck, each a healthy 110 to 120 pounds. It's a cavernous trunk—a real-sized trunk, the kind of trunk they don't make anymore, the kind of trunk you could throw a couple of deer into and still have room for a couple more. I grab one foreleg and roll one of the deer over. Then I clutch one of the ears and maneuver so I can see the diameter of the pupil.

When I grasp the front leg and move the deer, I am evaluating the amount of rigor mortis in the limbs. When an animal dies, all the muscles in the body relax because there is no stimulus to make them operate. All sphincters in the body relax and open. Depending on the state of bladder and bowel, this can be odiferous as well as messy. The muscles controlling your stomach, your esophagus, and your pupils are also sphincter muscles, therefore your pupils dilate upon death.

Rigor mortis is due to a biochemical change in the muscles that occurs several hours after death. The time of its onset depends on the size of the animal and the ambient temperature. Immediately after death the pupils are fixed and dilated the eyes appear moist and firm. All of the muscles completely relax and move smoothly and easily. Two to four hours after death, rigor mortis, combined with a lack of fluids, begins to stiffen the muscles and the eyes begin to look dull, less reflective. When you dry out leather it shrinks. Rigor mortis begins in the extremities and works into the larger muscle groups.

If I were in uniform, I would document current temperature and the temperature deep into one of the thigh muscles, and add that in with the results of an electronic stimulus test, which I could perform by hooking some probes to my truck battery and recording the degree of muscle contraction. I could tell you within the hour what time these deer were shot. Except, I'm not in uniform. I'm in the Special Investigations Unit. And when you're undercover you have to learn new ways to get the info you need to make your case. So I just go ahead and ask. "What time did you kill them?"

"Why do you care?" Norman Jr. replies.

"Because I want to make sure the deer are fresh. I don't know who the fuck you are. These could be three-day-old roadkills, for all I know."

"Hey, man, I ain't trying to rip you off. We shot these two between three and four o'clock this morning. Just ask Petey. He knows."

"Well," I reply, "I can't say I admire your choice of a reference."

We give the Silvers $150 for two does and load them, along with the ATV. Then we pay Rossi $200 for the three-wheeler and head back to "The Island" to start the paperwork and evidence logging.

As soon as we get back, I call James R. Beard, head of the SIU. "Hey, boss, we bought that three-wheeler today."

"What d'you pay for it?"

"Two grand," I reply.

Dead silence. Wojtecki is sitting beside me with his elbows on his knees, shaking his head and laughing. Through the phone, you can hear the gears turning in Jim's head, along with the shuffling of papers on his desk.

Finally, he says, "Now, you know I ain't that dumb, Mikey. If you're starting to slip, I am going to have to reel you in."

"He asked for two-fifty, we gave him two. It is worth a grand."

"Good. You got some numbers for me?"

I read him the serial number that was stamped into the frame.

Then, after some paper rattling I hear him say, "Bingo! Guy from Andreas reported it stolen on June 17."

///////////////////////////////

The early morning woods are bottom-of-the-tar-bucket black. I am lying face down on the frozen bank on the low side of a log-loading area in Downtown Nowhere. Just to my left lies Woj, holding his breath, as am I, to prevent the frozen water vapor from intersecting the flashlight beam that is mere inches above our sorry asses. The man in control of the light beam is wearing a pair of boots that are currently just a few centimeters above and forward of my head—the head in which a little voice whispers, "Momma, come get your baby boy!"

Woj and I, both covered head-to-toe in camouflage, have no idea how Mr. Flashlight Holder has yet failed to notice the two misplaced lumps sprawled before him. We both know that if our fogged breath crosses paths with the stream of light radiating from the flashlight, it will belie our presence, and the flashlight holder's reaction is only a matter of speculation.

////////////////////////////

A gunshot roars—KA-POW!—the blast knocking the turkey off its feet.

"You wait here," yells the hunting guide, as he leaps to his feet and charges to grab the bird as its wings thud their dirge. Even though he is shouting, the hunter does not understand what the guide has said. The shockwave created by his weapon causes tinnitus, and all he gets is faint, garbled noise.

"Yeah, buddy," the guide says, approaching us. "He's a beauty, all right. Prob'ly go twenty-one, twenty-two pounds."

"What's that around his leg?" asks the hunter.

"Oh, just some dewberry vines," says the guide, chuckling. "Just got hisself a might tangled up here."

That is pretty much how the would-be hunter explains the scenario when he calls Jim to register his complaint/concern about the hunting guide's business practices.

////////////////////////////

Jim Beard is a big man with a low growl and piercing green eyes that can warm you or freeze you, depending on their owner's mood and intentions. He's smart with an unrivaled sense of humor, and he's an easy man to spend time with. Jim recruited me early in my career, and as my direct superior he's earned my respect by always having my backside covered. We both know each other has a good hold on opposing ropes tied to the same tiger, and neither of us will ever let go.

Jim sits behind his disheveled desk on the edge of his chair, chewing an unlit stub of cigar, his green eyes fixed on his computer screen. "Hey, Mikey," he says, "I want you and Woj to take a look at this guy." He has his way with his keyboard a few more times and continues with his lifelong acquired Pennsylvania-Dutch, country boy accent. "There is something goin' on here." More tapping, then he pauses. "This Sandy Hollow hunting guide service advertises guided wild-turkey hunts with 100-percent success." He leans back in his chair, folds his bear-paw-sized hands over his belt buckle, and shifts the cigar stub to the other side of his mouth. "Unless he's talking about Wild Turkey bourbon, that's impossible. I just did a little checking here, and Sandy Hollow also has one of our wild turkey propagation permits."

A permit is a contract that makes exceptions to a law or regulation. It allows, under clearly defined conditions and circumstances, the holder to do certain activities antithetical contrary to that law or regulation under clearly defined conditions and circumstances.

Since Pennsylvania regulations prohibit the possession of live wild turkeys, they may only be lawfully possessed after scoring a permit from the PGC.

Jim leans forward, elbows on his knees. "This turd is either baiting wild birds or staking those pen-raised birds to the ground and taking his clients out there to give 'em a case of lead poisoning."

Not all of our cases are long, deep-cover, assumed-identity adventures. We primarily deal with commercialization cases, and we have the specialized cameras, recording, and surveillance equipment essential to gather evidence and intelligence. This is not likely to be one of those headline-news making, multi-state bombshells. Baiting wild turkeys is unlawful in PA, and while the turkey propagation permit allows the raising, possession, and sale of turkeys, the permit-holder is explicitly prohibited from releasing the birds into the wild. Or, as in this case, tying them down to simulate a "hunt".

After communicating our newest instruction from the boss, I say to Woj, "This sounds like a case for the Better Business Bureau. But we have received our marching orders, so…"

Woj and I, simultaneously exclaim, "March on!"

Sure, we have a plan. First, we will move furtively into the Sandy Hollow property. Next, we capture forever on film the guide placing the turkey in the woods before he "guides" the unsuspecting client back to shoot the ill-fated fowl. After that, we sidle out of the property with the evidence we will then use against the perpetrator in a court of law. The plan is simple, but so are we. For our scheme, as the Scottish poet Bobby Burns penned in *To a Mouse*, inevitably goes "agley."

And it's this "agley" scheme that has led Wojtecki and me to where we now lie. Faces pressed into the frozen ground, in the pitch-black night, holding our collective breaths just inches from a man searching with a flashlight, hoping, praying that he does not see us. Here we are risking lord knows what on a case that should've been forwarded to the BBB. *You better hope that guy with the flashlight doesn't decide to take a piss right now,* I think. What I want most, what we both need most, is to breathe.

"I didn't think that lame-dick asshole was ever going to leave," Woj huffs out in cloud-like, icy plumes, trying to catch his breath as Mr. Flashlight Man hoists himself into the vintage Ford pickup in which he arrived and departs. "What the fuck was he looking for anyway?"

"I couldn't read his mind," I say, "although I feel like I was close enough to."

"You were close enough to suck his dick, and I was afraid we were gonna have to in order to get out of this one."

"What do you mean *we*?" I fire back as we listen to the dwindling sounds of the man's tires crunching the frosted earth. "I reckon he was trying to see where he had tied or was going to tie one of those sorry turkeys to the ground."

"I don't know how that turkey farmer didn't see my big ass. There wasn't squat for cover."

"I don't know how he didn't smell you. Just think if he *had* seen you!"

Woj does not so much as even pause at my query as his brows rise in time with the corners of his mouth. "If he had seen me lying there," he says, "I was going to jump up, punch that fucker right in the fuckin' melon, and then haul ass."

I laugh. "Christ, Woj, I think this situation would demand a tad more diplomacy. Besides you're all ass. It would take you two trips."

"Don't quit your day job, funny boy. What would you have preferred?"

"I would have preferred not to to be on this wild turkey chase at zero dark thirty in the friggin' morning."

Woj rubs his right eye with his fist, bawling, "Whaaaa!"

"It's not like we had a lot of time to think about it," I say, spreading my arms to indicate the vastness of foliage encompassing us. "I mean, with all these acres of woods, what are the odds that dude was going to step on us?"

"For the rest of the population, one in a million. With our luck, three to one against."

I shake my head. "If he had, I was ready to spin an endearing tale about two dumb city boys who missed the posted signs because it was dark and we were stupid."

"Speak for yourself," says Woj.

"Well, we couldn't claim to be hunting, sans shotguns."

"What the hell's a sand shotgun?"

"Saaans. S-A-N-S, you fuck stick! It means without."

"Excuse me, Mr. Merriam fucking Webster!"

I roll my eyes. "Listen, you dumb blockhead, Merriam and Webster were *two* people, not one person. Now shut your doughnut hole."

"OK. Just don't say doughnut. You're making me hungry."

I continue to tell Woj how I would have told the man we were hunting for early spring mushrooms and/or scouting for turkeys. I had used mushroom hunting as an excuse for being somewhere on other occasions, and I knew enough to cover my ass if the inquisitor happened to be a mycologist. Wild mushrooms are favored by gourmet chefs, and one can make a tidy sum if he knows what to look for and where to find them. "I would have gone with the mushroom story though, since scouting for turkeys might've pissed him off, given it appears they augment his income."

"They what his income?"

"Augment," I say. "He makes money off of them."

"Oh, why don't you just speak English?"

"Here's some English for you: FUCK YOU!"

The SIU purchased a full-size VCR camera to document evidence and film transactions in parking lots and side roads, under bridges and trees. Before that, whenever we scheduled a buy or take down, we'd employ the services of Hal Korber, the game commission's audio/video specialist. Hal shot hours of footage that was used to help prosecute a number of suspects. The problem is he had a real job all the way back in Harrisburg and wasn't always available.

I am building my house at this time, so I have myriad cardboard boxes scattered about. What I'm looking for is a box big enough to hide a suitcase-sized VCR camera, with room for protective padding. A toilet-tank box will do the trick. You know, the kind with holes poked in the sides to facilitate lifting it. After making a few adjustments to one of the holes, I have what I need. Almost. The box does the trick, but at the right angle, you can still see the camera lens. So I go to the auto parts store, purchase window tinting film and secure a piece of it on the inside of the box. It allows the camera to see out, but no one can see in.

I am in the headquarters basement working on this when I get buzzed by Jayne, my boss' secretary. "The boss needs to see you," she says.

Ugh.

It isn't that I don't enjoy spending time with Jim. He's the best boss I've ever had. He's intelligent, quick-witted, and is one of the funniest people I've ever met. Jim can spin a yarn that would leave you breathless with laughter. I just don't like going upstairs. It's not that I'm paranoid or afraid. I only want to minimize my degree of risk. People go in and out of PGC headquarters all the time. If someone we're investigating, or someone who knows them was to see me in that building, it would ruin the investigation and waste all of the money and time we've invested in the case.

I walk into Jim's office as he is moving piles of paper around on his desk searching for the right one.

"What are you doing here?" he asks.

"Jayne said you needed to see me." There are two chairs directly in front of his desk. I choose the one nearer the window and sit down.

"Watch this," he says, leaning back in his chair and clicking a couple of switches. The dead screen on the monitor facing me in the middle of his desk begins to come to life. Suddenly, I see a live version of my face. I wave my hand through the air, trying figure out where the hidden camera is.

Finally I see a small box sitting on his window sill, about the size of a cigarette lighter, with two wires running out of the bottom. "One for power and one for video," I say.

Jim smiles and nods in the affirmative. "I went up to Steve Williams (the Deputy Executive Director) and showed him some of the work you guys are doing with what little you have. He loved the videos, so he added more money to the SI Unit to buy miniature cameras and recorders. I need you to go through this magazine and pick out the stuff you could use."

Remember, this is all taking place in the 1990s, before cell phones had cameras and everything you can think of is miniaturized. Hell, few people even *have* cell phones at this time. Back then, most of this tech was stuff you'd still only see in movies. Yet the catalogue that my boss just handed me has hundreds of cameras, lenses, wires—all of the equipment I need to develop a line of hidden cameras to film some of the worst law breakers.

From that moment on, I put cameras inside boxes, bags, fire sprinklers, fire alarms, jackets, fishing vests, dome lights, vehicle brake lights, and spotlights. I even place a concealed camera inside a ball cap.

//////////////////////////////

I saunter into Jim's office and look at the sign on the wall: IF A CLUTTERED DESK SIGNIFIES A CLUTTERED MIND, WHAT DOES AN EMPTY DESK MEAN?

"Mikey," he says, "how'd you make out with the information the *Feds* provided?" Jim, who's not a fan of the US Fish and Wildlife Service, emphasizes the word "Feds."

"The information was spot on," I say. "The guy says he has thirty-four California bear galls he'll sell me."

Bear gallbladders are a highly valued commodity in the Asian markets. One gall can fetch thousands of dollars. Because the black market is so lucrative, some miscreants will even try to pass off pig gallbladders as bear.

I tell Jim how I agreed to meet the seller at the same hotel next week and buy the fourteen he has at home. Then, if those galls check out, I'll make plans to buy twenty more.

"MONGO!" he replies, in typical Jim Beard style. One of his favorite words, it could be veneration or condemnation, depending on his mood and the circumstance.

"I need ten thousand to make the deal," I say.

"MONGO, fuck! You sure they're all bear?"

"Gave me his word. Of course, that depends on how much you value the word of a poacher-slash-turd. He's a hound hunter. Runs his dogs in northern California, mostly spring bears. He's fairly well off. Says he just wants to sell the bear galls to make some cash to pay for more hunting trips."

"I don't think California has a spring bear season."

"That's good thinking, boss. I already checked it, and you're right—they don't."

After I buy the gallbladders, Jim contacts California Department of Fish and Wildlife Game[1] to let them know they may want to check on this guy. One of their officers is a young man by the name of Joe Knarr. He and the rest of the folks from the California agency say there is no way the parts I purchased are bear galls. Nobody had ever bought that many bear gallbladders in one deal. Surely, I had purchased pig gallbladders. To be certain I have them

---

1 They are called California Department of Fish and Wildlife now.

tested at our State Police Crime Lab, and the lab confirms they are indeed *Ursus americanus*—black bear. They're still dubious. So, I box them all up and send them to California. After running their own tests they agree that every one of them is a bear gallbladder.

Sometime after that Joe Knarr transfers to Montana Fish Wild- life & Parks Special Investigations Unit, where he and I make a very successful undercover case that leads all the way to Africa. We become good friends. Tragically, he dies much too young. Victim of a heartbreaking murder-suicide.

PART II

TIMBER PIRATES

There are no microphones or any other equipment or device on my person or in my vehicle capable of recording conversations with anyone. Section 5703 of the Pennsylvania Wiretapping and Electronic Surveillance Control Act, aka the "Wiretap Act," makes it illegal to record private conversations, including conversations in public places, without the consent of all parties involved in that conversation (or a warrant, and we'll get to that). Anyone with a camera may capture images in public places, but that right does not extend to capture what people say. It is not always lawful to record the spoken word. Conversations with police in the course of their duties are not private conversations, but many other things you might want to record are.

There are numerous devises used to record or listen to conversations. In the Commonwealth of Pennsylvania, state law makes it unlawful to even possess said equipment or devices, with few exceptions. Pennsylvania State Police Bureau of Criminal Investigations is authorized to loan the equipment to an officer, only if the officer has completed an extensive training program and received a Class A certification in wiretapping and intercepting oral communications. While an officer with a Class A certification is authorized to use the equipment, they may only possess it while working on a specific case. In Pennsylvania, intercepting or recording any wire, oral, or electronic communication without the consent of the person or persons being recorded is a felony of the third degree, even for law enforcement officers outside of their normal course of duties.

Laws differ in the United States on how many parties must give their consent before a conversation may be recorded. In thirty-eight states and the District of Columbia, conversations may be recorded if the person is party to the conversation, or if at least one of the people who are party to the conversation have given consent to a third-party to record the conversation. In California, Connecticut, Delaware, Florida, Illinois, Maryland, Maine, Massachusetts, Nevada, New Hampshire, Pennsylvania, Vermont, and Washington State, the consent of *all* parties of the conversation must be obtained in order to record a conversation.

I first learn all of this, let's say, the hard way.

Back in our training academy, I'd requested to work in the SIU. I thought it might be an interesting challenge and at the time we had no one working in that unit. My request was granted. A little before graduation, however, the officer in the northern Adams County unexpectedly retired. The powers that be reasoned, or unreasoned, that filling a uniformed officer's vacant position was better for the agency's image than filling an empty special investigator (SI) position. There were four SI positions in the unit still unfilled, and there was plenty of information to work on.

My first year in uniform my very first assignment is northern Adams County, Pa., about thirty minutes from Harrisburg. Soon after I arrive I get good information that a local butcher in Garrett's Market is selling venison mixed in with his ground-beef. This would be a fantastic case for an undercover officer, but we don't have any undercover officers. I've only been in my new district a few weeks, and not many people know what I look like. So, I decide not to shave for a couple of days, go into into Garrett's, and buy some meat to send to the crime lab for testing. The form I complete when I submit the meat for analysis finds its way to Jim Beard's desk.

Back at my house, the phone rings. I pick up the

headset and answer, “Mike Dubaich.”

I hear that familiar, deep baritone voice conflated with a Pennsylvania Dutch accent. “Hey, Mikey, what are you doing down there?”

“My job. Why? Is someone complaining?”

“What’s going on with this deer meat?”

“Don’t worry. I have it bagged and tagged in my freezer, which only I have access to because I live alone.”

“How are you paying for it?”

“That is one hell of a question,” I answer. Then I reply, “With my own cash, not Game Commission money if that’s what you are asking.”

Jim is silent, as if he’s pondering his next move, then he asks, “What are you going to do when your three years are up?” Back then, newly appointed officers had to remain in the districts they’re assigned to for at least three years before requesting a transfer.

“I’m heading northwest,” I reply. “Forest County, if I can.”

“There ain’t nothing to do up there, Mikey. You’ll be bored as hell. You should come to Harrisburg and help me build a new special investigations unit. There hasn’t been anyone working SI for eight years, and we have tons of good information.”

“I’ll think on it.”

"In the meantime," he says, "if you want to make a little overtime, and because you seem to want to start your own one-man team, I want you to check some case information."

/////////////////////////////

In the mid-80's, Larry Harshaw is the law enforcement supervisor for the south-central region. Adams County is located within the boundaries of the region, thereby making Harshaw my supervisor. He is one of the people who lifts me and inspires me early in my career. While completing my first-year employee performance review, he writes, "Mike is fast becoming one of the finest officers in the game commission." His words give me the encouragement and inspiration to continue working hard. Everyone likes a bit of recognition once in a while.

Harshaw asks me to travel with Don Barker to see if we can gather some intelligence about the rampant timber theft currently plaguing the area. Don is one of the dispatchers in the region, and when I'm on patrol I rely on him to get me the information or help if I need it He is also a deputy, so he knows how it feels to be on each side of the radio. He is good company, and we easily become good friends.

Because I am the closest thing the agency has to a full-time special investigator, and because Don has proven himself as a deputy and dispatcher and is familiar with the territory, they bring the two of us together and turn us loose on the world. This new duty does not relieve me of my old one, however. It means a lot more driving time and some long days and nights.

Timber prices were rising, which meant more timber was showing up at the sawmills. It also meant more men looking for trees to cut down, whether they own the timber or not. Our mission, which we chose to accept, is to infiltrate this timber-cutting, log-hauling society and discover who's doing what, with what, and to whom.

We have a pre-investigation meeting at the south-central office in Huntingdon the second week of August, mainly to make sure everybody knows what is expected. Harrisburg will supply the funds, and Don and I agree to report verbally to Larry Harshaw on a daily basis. Thankfully, Don agrees to complete the Report of Investigation forms. He knows how busy I am in this, my first fall as a game warden. I have enough paperwork to do already.

As everybody is preparing to leave, I shout out, "Hey, gentlemen! Before you go, we need something to drive." Their collective response, or lack thereof, leads me to believe that none of them had given any consideration to this. Turns out, the SIU has one old Chevy pickup with confidential plates on it. Jim tells me to leave my marked vehicle out back by the loading docks and to use the unmarked truck to get around while I'm working on the timber case.

The old Chevy has seen better days for sure, but it starts easily and runs smoothly. It also has a fresh coat of shiny black paint that hides where the Game Commission stickers use to be. Inside, the doors and jams are still green, and so is the underside of the hood and wheel wells.

Unimpressed with the paint job, I say to Don, "Since we're here at the office, let's get that plate number off the back and run it."

"Ten four," Don replies.

"And *that* is the last time I want to hear that today."

"Ten four," he says, laughing.

"Another fucking wise guy."

Then, as Don starts to walk away, I tell him to check the VIN, too. "If it doesn't come back 'Department of General Services,' I'll buy the first round."

There are specific words and phrases that people associate with law enforcement and I've always tried to avoid using that lingo when I can. Words such as "vehicle" or "motor vehicle," should just be "car" or "truck." I don't say "sidearm or firearm" I say "pistol" or "gun." And never, ever use the word "operator" unless you are taking about the telephone.

A little while later, Don comes walking over to where I'm standing.

"What do you have?" I ask.

"You were right," he says. "The plate number came back as 'confidential,' and the VIN says the Department of General Services owns the truck."

"Goddamn it. All right, at least we know what we're dealing with. There's nothing we can do about that now. It'll be a little time before anyone tries to check us out."

I walk over to the garage and come back with a hammer and some grease on an old rag. I smear the grease on the license plate and then proceed to hammer the aluminum plate, making it look like it's been hit numerous times by someone backing into a trailer hitch. After that, I toss a little dust and dirt on it, which the grease nicely grabs. "There," I say. "Patina."

Don looks dubious. "What if we get stopped?"

"What do you mean *we*? I ain't driving this thing anywhere with that plate on the back." Of course, I'm grinning too much to be serious.

"Come on, Deputy Barker. Let's go fight crime. I'll even drive."

As we drive away, I tell him not to worry. "If we get

stopped, we just play dumb. I don't know you all that well but playing dumb comes natural to me. In the meantime, if anyone wants to get a look at your plate number, and I did say *your* plate number, they are going to have to wipe off some of that grease and dirt. We see the grease has been messed with, we'll know we have someone's attention."

We spend the rest of the day going to log yards and checking prices. As we approach yard number five, I decide to test Don on what we've learned.

"Well," he replies, "we've learned the log buying yards are not hard to find. Just look for mud, trucks, and logs."

"And," I add, just as Barker bounces the pickup into the log yard, "we confirmed the only trees worth time getting are oak, black cherry, and white ash."

The log yard is buzzing with activity. "Holy shit," I shout, just to be heard over the screech of the big mill saw ripping the trees into boards, "this place is hopping!"

There are two men wearing helmets and face masks and wielding chainsaws. They slash into logs, throwing plumes of sawdust rooster tails behind them. Huge green logging skidders bounce by on deeply treaded balloon tires, looking like giant green beetles wobbling along. A yellow forklift cradles a log and drops it into the waiting maw of the bark peeler.

I'm straining to be heard over the industrial din and

deafening noise. "Whenever I hear people with office jobs talk about how tough they have it at work," I say, turning to Don, "I tell them try working in a sawmill. First you have the logs. Logs roll over you. They can fall on you or be dragged over you…"

Meanwhile, we're both looking for a man carrying what looks like a wooden yard stick but is actually a log scale.

"There he is," says Don, pointing, "on the other side of that big lake of mud."

In one hand the man is holding a clipboard with his log rule. In the other he has a large stick of yellow grease paint. It looks like a giant yellow crayon. He measures each log's length and diameter and then uses those figures to estimate the number of board feet in a particular log. Having reached that figure, he marks the butt end of the log with that number.

"Hey," I say to Don, "you didn't let me to finish my dangerous log yard story."

"You can enlighten me later," he replies. "Let's see what this fella has to say." At this point the yard boss is waving us to come across the mud lake. "How deep you think that is?"

"Too deep to walk through, that's for sure. Drive our asses over there and let's talk with this gentleman."

Moments later we're out of the truck and standing in

front of the yard boss.

"And how may I help you two young men on this fine afternoon?" he says with a slight bow and a sweep of his left arm. He kicks the side of his rubber boots against the log closest to him. "Come to buy some mud?"

"Naw," I reply, "the mud market is a little soft right now. Don't get me wrong, you have some nice mud up here. You should be very proud."

"Well, thank you kindly," the man says as he tucks his thumbs behind his South Park suspenders. "What can I do you for?"

"We're driving around looking for some prices. My name's Don and the dumb one here is Mike."

"It's a pleasure to meet you both. They call me Butch. Let's go over to my office and I'll get you a price list."

Just outside the pay office, we read the photocopy listing of the prices. "What's a billet?" I ask, pointing at the 8 ½" x 14" sheet of paper.

"Well," Butch begins, "a few years back the big lumber yards began to offer custom stair treads and custom railing. The stair treads were only forty inches long and the railing was forty inches. The red oak logs were cut up into forty-two-inch logs called billets." He goes on to tell us that, at first, they would buy eight-and-a-half-foot logs and cut them in two. The problem is, he says, you lose most of the value when you cut them in half, and no person with an eight-foot log is going to risk hundreds of dollars by cutting it in two.

Butch is looking at us as if he wants to be sure we were paying attention, then he continues. "Soon the demand for the billets couldn't be filled. Of course, the price goes up too."

"Of course," Don and I reply in unison, which makes Butch smile.

"No one will sell their logs at half price or less," he says, "but if you sell someone else's logs, you can run a pretty low overhead. All you need to operate your business is a pickup truck, a chain saw, a couple of ramps, and some nice red oak trees uphill from your truck."

"So you think the billets are stolen?" I ask.

"I'd say 99 percent of them are. No one of sound mind would cut a beautiful oak into pieces. The very act itself should be criminal."

Don and I look at each other and nod in agreement.

"But am *I* guilty of some crime?" Butch continues. "Here in the United States of America, every person is innocent until proven guilty. There is no chance the authorities have any evidence that could prove beyond a reasonable doubt I knew any of the billets were stolen at the time that I bought, possessed or sold them. Any prosecutor who tried to convince a judge otherwise would be wasting taxpayers' money."

"What are you," I ask, "a lawyer or something?"

Butch chuckles. "No, not quite. I'm just a retired high-school history teacher with a brother who died too soon from the big C. I could have sold this place, but that would have ruined the lives of the eight hard working people who were dedicated to my brother."

"Damn," Don adds, "sawmills are a—"

"Hard way to make a living?" Butch cuts him off. "Yeah, well they do all the hard work. All I do is count the logs and pay the money."

A little while later Don and I are back out on the main road.

//////////////////////////////

Our day complete, we head back to Huntingdon. I still have a two-hour drive home and some night patrol on the schedule.

"Be out tonight, Mike?"

"You bet," I reply. "The farmers were picking corn when I left."

For those of you wondering, at night deer come out of hiding and into the field to eat any corn that was knocked to the ground when the picker came crashing through. And with the corn stalks gone, for the first time in months you can look far into the fields from the road. Poaching was about to begin in earnest.

"I'll keep an ear out for you," says Don. "I'm on dispatch from eighteen-hundred to zero two-hundred. Be careful out there."

///////////////////////////

We stay away from the mill the next day and then head out the day after, this time more prepared with the tools of the trade. When I pull into the fenced-in lot where our vehicles are being stored, I watch as Don places his chainsaw, one gallon of premixed gasoline, and one gallon of bar-and-chain oil into the bed of our undercover truck.

"Nice saw," I say, walking around to the bed. "Where'd you steal that one?"

"I didn't steal anything. Borrowed it from Harv."

"Does Harv know?"

"Well, not exactly."

"Borrowing without telling someone is stealing," I tell him.

"Well, it's not really Harvey's. It's owned by the game

commission. Harvey is just the only one who uses it."

"Until now."

"Look," he says, "I am not going to risk my personal chainsaw being stolen or smashed by a tree or run over by a truck."

"Relax, big boy," I reply, grabbing my own saw. "You make a good point. Just make sure there isn't an equipment number stuck on it somewhere."

"Oh, yeah. I hadn't thought of that." Then, after looking it over closely, he says, "Here it is!" shaking his head and peeling the sticker off. "Just like the man said it would be."

It's my turn to drive and later we're traveling south on Route 350 through Phillipsburg. Just then Don swats my arm with the back of his hand and exclaims, "There they are!"

"There who are?"

During our recent travels, Don and I twice saw a vintage, light-blue Ford F-150 pickup with rust trim. The original bed had long since rotted off its frame, and it had carefully been refurbished with a flat bed of oak planks framed on three sides by two-by-six boards, standing on edge. In the bed we could see two chainsaws—one Stihl and one Husqvarna—along with two heavy oak planks, each about eight feet in length; an array of plastic bottles; one length of chain; and one frayed and tattered nylon strap, yellow in color. Was it the same truck we were looking at now—one of four vehicles sitting in the parking lot of the Phillipsburg branch of the American Legion?

"You think that's it?" asks Don, certain it was.

"I believe it is, my friend. And it looks like it's carrying a little extra weight this morning."

That extra weight is in the form of four cylinders of red oak, forty-two inches tall and thirty-six inches across. I maneuver the old Chevy into the parking lot and pull front-in between the two yellow stripes, immediately adjacent to the old Ford. As I do, Don gives me one of those *What-the-fuck-are-you-doing?* looks. I try to ease his mind. "I know, there are plenty of other parking spots in here. But I have two reasons for my parking selection, should they ask."

Don smiles. "Go on."

"Immediately, my good man. First, we tell 'em we're strangers in town. People are inquisitive, anxious, worried even. Parking so close, A) gives them a relatively safe opportunity to quote-unquote check us out, and B) gives us the chance to engage them and gather some intelligence."

Even before we get out of the truck, we can see the Ford is severely overloaded. The leaf springs are sprung flat or even a little past flat. The rear tires are bulging under the strain, and the front tires are barely touching the ground. If not for the weight of the two passengers in the bucket seats, the truck couldn't even get out of the lot.

As we walk toward the bar, we can hear lively banter emanating from within. I pull the door open and step back to allow Don to enter. The bright sunlight washes into the dark barroom, and as the door closes, the light washes back out like a wave on speed.

The level of conversation between the eight or ten patrons is akin to walking near a pond full of spring peepers. When they hear or see you, their cacophony abruptly ceases. As you walk away, one begins chirping again, followed by another, culminating in a viral crescendo.

Don and I walk over to the bar, and as I rest my elbows on the brass railing fronting the bar, the bartender asks, "What can I get for you fellows?"

"A couple of bibles," I reply, which abruptly stops all conversation in the room.

The lady barkeep hesitatingly replies, "I'm sorry, mister, but we don't have any of those."

"Well," I say, "just give us a couple Iron City bottles, then."

Don gives me a look. "What are you doing, Mike? Trying to get us thrown out of another bar?" Then he turns to the bartender. "I apologize for him, ma'am. What little manners he has are all bad."

I turn to Don with my middle finger pointed down to

the floor. "Can you hear that?"

"No," he says, then adds, "I know, I know, turn it up for me. Jesus, Mike, that wasn't funny the first hundred times you told it."

The bar atmosphere is pretty standard for 90 percent of the bars in the US: a back wall covered with mirrors and booze bottles, with a service entrance on each end of a U-shaped bar with accompanying stools. Don and I are seated in the middle with our backs to the empty tables and chairs. On our right, facing the door, sit three men and a woman who look like third shifters, aka people who work the midnight-to-8-a.m. shift. To those night birds, this is happy hour, analogous to 5 p.m. for workers whose hours are 8 to 4 or 9 to 5.

On the left side of the bar, sitting with their backs to the door, we have three people, one of which is a lone man who looks like he's been on the outside of too many bottles in his lifetime. That means the two gentlemen seated in the middle on the left side have to be our boys. They are currently holding a conversation with the bartender. They call her Janice and she doesn't correct them. The two guys we are looking for are Bud and Lou, but we have no idea which was which.

"Janice!" I call out. "A round for the house."

"And I was just about to throw these two bums out,"

she says, her thumb pointed at our boys.

"Now why would you go and do something like that?" Bud or Lou says.

"Because" says Janice, "when you two wandered in here, you told me you were just killing time. You said your truck was loaded, and you couldn't do anything until the sawmill opened and you could drop off your load. That was a-quarter-to-eight, and I know the mill opens at eight."

"What time is it now?" asks Bud or Lou.

"10:30," says Janice.

I cannot miss this opportunity. "If that blue Ford out there is theirs," I say, "it's definitely packing heavy. That baby is loaded."

Don and I finish our second beer of the morning, as if we did this every day. Then, from across the bar, I tell our new friends, "Our truck on the other hand, unlike yours, is *not* full and we need to change that, A-SAP." Then we head out the door.

I have never liked walking out of a bar and into the daylight. It's an assault on the senses. This must be how a vampire feels. I am barely regaining my sight when the door to the Legion opens, and out pour Bud and Lou. They are quiet until they lay their eyes on our truck. When they see our run-down, freshly painted truck, complete with a bed full of saws, chains, gas, and oil, they have no doubt we're the real deal.

"We've seen you guys running the roads," one of them says.

"Where you loggin'?" Asks the other one.

I stick out my hand. "I'm Mike. That one riding with me is Don. We've been working south of here, mostly game lands."

"They have so much ground they can't take care of it," adds Don. "Way we see it we're just helping them do their jobs. Things have been getting a little hot down there, though, so we figured we'd move up north a little."

"They call me Lou, and this here is my partner and lover, Merle. But he answers to Bud."

"I ain't your lover, you pecker head! You better stop saying that." Then Bud turns back to us. "We have a nice spot all lined up, but there's a chance we might get stuck."

"I hate those ruts," I reply.

Lou takes over. "If you have one truck and stick it, you're fucked. But if you have another truck with you, you can help each other out. Hopefully."

"You guys have a three-quarter ton," says Bud. "It can haul a hell of a lot more wood than our little Ford. Deer season starts in two or three weeks, so if we cut at all, it better be a good spot."

"The weather's been dry," says Lou. "The way in ain't

gonna get any better, so let's do it tomorrow."

"Tomorrow," echoes Bud.

"Sounds good," Don and I reply in concert.

///////////////////////////////

"Tomorrow!?" Larry Harshaw is not happy. "You guys have no back-up. No cover officers. What about private land? Do you even have the authority to go onto private property and steal someone's trees? What if the landowner, or his neighbor, hates tree thieves and decides to shoot you numb-headed assholes?"

"We don't need back-up," I say. "Don has my back, and I have his. But you make a good point about the getting shot thing. We never even thought about that."

"What time did they say to be there?" asks Larry.

"Zero six-hundred," Don replies.

"It's already almost four. Why don't you guys just grab a hotel and stay here tonight?"

"No can do, boss," I say. "I've got the Adams County Fish and Game meeting at twenty-hundred." Then, turning to Don, "I will see you at zero five-hundred, Mr. Barker."

///////////////////////////////

"D'you get any sleep?" Don asks me, as I climb into

the passenger side of the Chevy pickup.

"Didn't even try," I say. "Too excited, too nervous, too—"

"Scared."

"A little," I say, yawning. "But I'm not worried about those two weasels. We're going to steal timber in north central Pennsylvania. It's the landowners who worry me. They'll hang us first, then shoot us."

Smiling now, Don drives north.

We pull into the Legion parking lot at zero five-fifty hours. Bud and Lou's truck is parked in the lot, but contains no occupants. "If you're not ten minutes early, you're late," I say.

I hear Don muttering to no one, "Christ, those fucking guys sleep here?"

We gather our presence and walk into the bar. There is no waiting for our eyes to adjust.

Janice immediately recognizes us. "Hey, big guy," she says to me, "you found those bibles yet?"

"Not yet. But I don't discourage easily," I reply with a smile.

I look at Bud and Lou, each with white paper coffee cups centered on the bar in front of them. I would not be going out on a limb if I thought there was a little snakebite medicine in those cups, but it looks like it's mostly coffee.

"If you're getting coffee, get it to go," growls Lou.

"He sounds like all business today," I say to Don.

When we walk outside, all Lou says is, "Follow us."

So that's just what we do.

The sun is rising off to my right, so I know we're going north even before we pass a road sign indicating we are indeed on Route 350 North. When the road turns east, we do not. Instead, we continue on a road with no painted lines to a four-way stop, where we turn right, travel up hill to a low ridge top, then start downhill.

The sun is mostly up by now, and we're about halfway down the ridge when we see Bud and Lou's brake lights glow as the right turn signal starts blinking. The turn puts us on a well-maintained gravel driveway. We pass a sign that reads PRIVATE ROAD. All the better. No traffic. Less than a quarter mile later, the driveway makes a right. Halfway around this bend, we turn left going off road, slightly downhill and swinging to the right. We are on an old log-skidder trail, and you can see why they needed it to be dry. The tires from the logging equipment have left some rather large ruts. As we continue down the overgrown trail, the road begins to flatten, and the ground looks softer.

I notice a little water is darkening the tires on the Ford in front of us, so when I feel like we're on a piece of rocky, slightly drier ground, I stop our truck to make sure Bud and Lou get through before I continue. There's no point in getting us both stuck. The trail then takes another turn and starts climbing up the side of the ridge.

Our boys are only about 300 yards up the sidehill when we stop on an old log-landing. On a slope like this there is no area level enough and large enough to give the logging trucks room to turn around, pick up a load, and go back out the way they came in. Using a bulldozer you move soil from the uphill side to the downhill side, basically creating a notch in the side of the hill. The size of the area depends on the degree of slope and the number of logs you need to stack. The level spot you create leaves a wall or bank going uphill. On the opposite side, you have a drop-off from where you are standing downhill to the original ground you have buried.

Lou makes a short U-turn and pulls up alongside of me as we each crank our windows down. "Drop your tailgate and back up against the bank," he tells me. "It's a little high on the left and a little low on the right," he says, pointing his finger. "Aim for the middle. Your tailgate should hit the bank a few inches below the ground."

Bud and Lou's truck is backing in a little to my left. Their truck is not quite as high as ours, and the slope isn't as steep where he's aiming his tailgate. As it rubs the forest floor, Lou presses in his clutch, hits the brakes, and yells, "BINGO!"

Don speaks first as we get out of the truck. "You guys sure can pick a spot. You've got plenty of room to maneuver. Downhill from trees to truck. And, ladies and gentlemen, look at those red oaks. Those big boys are straight as the road to hell and an axe handle wide."

Lou continues barking orders. "They may walk themselves into our trucks, but we gotta put 'em on the ground. Let's stop talkin' about it and make it so."

Lou grabs his saw as I pick up mine. After checking to be sure that my gas and bar-and- chain oil are both full, I walk up the hill behind our trucks to the first two red oaks where Lou is waiting.

Don and I had this discussion earlier. If someone gives us shit for cutting down trees on private property, I'll be the one to take the heat. I am the only full-time salaried officer on our team and, therefore, I should be the one held responsible for anything we fuck up.

"How many billets can you boys get on that truck?" he asks.

"Six, maybe seven," I reply, "depending on how big they are."

"I can carry three, and your seven makes ten. You think there are five good billets in that tree?"

"I will tell you right after it's lying on its side."

Lou leans against the tree. "I'll take this one. Try to drop the tops in the log landing. They'll be harder to see."

I nod.

"And don't hit the fucking trucks," he adds.

Turning trees into logs is treacherous work. Wielding 8 Kg/17.6 pounds of a screaming, two-cycle 91.6cc gasoline engine pushing 7.8 horsepower, with a chain that is moving at 55 to 60 m.p.h., or a mile per minute, is hazardous work. Every second 7.8 horses is dragging 88 feet of razor-sharp teeth and chain through wood, bone, or flesh. It is what it is, and it does what it does.

A mature red oak, thirty-six inches across, weighs between eight and nine tons. Felling one of these behemoths is equivalent to dropping a 15,000-pound hammer on the earth. It will crush and kill anything in its way. The sawyer must always be on guard for limbs, living or dead, that break off, fall off, or are torn off of the tree they are dropping, not to mention any trees your tree strikes or falls through. Loggers call these falling limbs "widow makers." Enough said.

Once the tree is on the ground, you start making billets. The more accurate you make your cuts, the less wood is wasted. The less wood is wasted, the more money you make. There are many ways to measure forty-two inches. Some guys carry a yard stick. Others, a stick forty-two inches long. Some prefer a standard tape measure, a folding stone mason's ruler, or even a length of clothesline or chord bearing a tag or mark every forty-two inches. You start at what was the base of the tree and measure up, making a mark on the log every forty-two inches. You always start at the bottom because that's where the biggest logs are. If you start from the smaller end of the log, you could end up with only forty or forty-one inches of log remaining. Anything under forty-two is wasted. The only thing it's good for is firewood.

I have my five billets on the ground and I turn to see how Lou is making out. He finishes his fourth cut through the log that, no more than five minutes ago, was a two-hundred-year-old oak tree. Lou leans into the saw as its carburetor calls for more fuel to feed the accelerating engine.The old green Husqvarna is throwing out huge wood chips and dust as it tears through the tree.

Don walks over and sits on one of the billets. "I have to ask him what type of chain he uses," he says. "That mother is sharp."

Bud walks over and says, "Same chain as everybody else. We just know the proper way to sharpen a saw."

Lou finishes what I think is his last cut. With his saw idling, he returns to the first billet he carved off of the red oak, studies the short log, revs up the saw, and proceeds to slice about two inches off the bottom of the log. This gives him a large oak Frisbee just under two inches thick, which he can easily break into pieces to be scattered about.

"We do it so they can't match any of our logs to these stumps," says Bud.

"Sneaky bastards," Don says to no one in particular.

The most perilous time for a billet cutter is when the saw is running. A chainsaw is a very noisy animal, and it will divulge your presence to the world. The more you hurry, the more likely it is that you'll injure yourself or others. While sawing, you have no idea of what is going on around you. You cannot hear if a vehicle is approaching or if the landowner is brandishing a gun and shrieking, "Get the fuck off of my property!" It is for that reason that someone in party acts as a lookout. In a two-man operation, while one man does the sawing, the other keeps an eye out for trouble. That means nobody is working on getting the billets on the truck.

The reason Bud and Lou are so eager to join up with Don and me is because four can work faster and more efficiently than two. With four bodies you can have two men sawing, one on the lookout, and the fourth moving the billet to the trucks. Each billet weighs between 700 and 900 pounds, which is why it's imperative you select trees that are slightly higher in elevation than your truck.

It is slightly downhill to our pickups, so rolling the billets is not the problem. The problem is getting them to turn. Don is struggling with a billet and is not strong enough to force it into a right turn. Bud limps over to Don and decides the billet makes a fine seat to take a break. Exasperated and exhausted, Don also sits on the log, with his elbows on his knees. Then he looks up at Bud and, between gasps for air, says, "How do you get… these mother-loving…goddamned logs…to go the way you want them to?"

I have finished my sawing at this point and I walk down to the truck to put my Stihl back. Some of the branches came a little closer than I had intended, so I jerk on the starting cord and the saw roars back to life. Stepping toward the branches, I reach out and cut a limb about three feet long and four inches thick. Then I toss it up the bank toward Don and Bud. Don picks it up and looks at me. "What am I supposed to do with this?" he says. "Beat on the log until it turns?"

"Why does every tool someone hands you become a hammer?" I reply. "It's pure physics. That stick I cut for you will be the fulcrum, the log a lever." I climb up the bank and Don hands me the branch. I tap each of his boots with it, saying, "Get your ass off my billet."

Don is unamused. "Get your own billet! This one is mine."

"Now, now, children," says Bud, "there are plenty of

billets for everyone."

Making my way to the uphill side of Don's billet, I take the branch and lay it perpendicular to the log. "That, ladies and gentlemen," I say, "is what you call a fulcrum. The billet becomes a lever. If you have the fulcrum in the exact center of the log, it will balance and both ends of the log will be off of the ground, similar to a teeter-totter."

I push the billet onto the branch and swivel it to the right 90 degrees. As you go up a tree, the trunk's diameter gets smaller. This particular log is lying downhill from my left to my right. Grabbing my tape, I measure the diameter. "The left side is just about thirty-two inches," I say, "and the right is just about thirty."

"So what's your point, pointy head?" Don replies.

"Allow me a minute, young man," I say. "In order to ascertain the circumference, you multiply by Pi..."

"By what?" asks Bud.

"We don't have the time," I respond.

"Why don't you just measure the circumference with your tape measure?" says Don, not helping.

Now I'm getting frustrated because the measuring isn't the point. I explain that, no matter how you get there, you will discover that the circumference of the bottom of the log (i.e., the left side) is 108, and the right side is 94. Each time you roll the log around one time, the left side will have traveled 108 inches, while the right side only 94. If you roll this billet unassisted, it can only turn toward the smaller side, in this case to the right.

Right about then Lou walks up brushing sawdust off his jacket, his ears still ringing from the strident buzz of the chainsaw. He and Bud do not subscribe to the idea of safety equipment, namely gloves, chaps, eye protection, helmets, and, in this instance, hearing protection. Yelling so he can hear himself in his head, he says, "Come on, girls. Break time is over. Let's get this wood loaded and get the fuck out of here."

Moments later we are loading the billets into the trucks when we hear that unmistakable sound that every country boy knows—the sound of automobile tires on gravel.

"Motherfucker," we all grumble in unison.

Bud affirms our fear. "Someone is coming up the driveway!"

We would scramble if we could, but there is nothing we can do to improve our situation. When whoever it is comes around the bend, they won't miss the two pickup trucks parked against the hillside in the middle of the woods. We can hear them approaching, and all we can do is listen and pray they'll miss us.

The low popping sound of gravel under tires grows

in volume, and we can hear as the truck—we all agree it has to be a truck—slows down for the curve. As it breaks around the corner, we see flickers of sunlight glancing off the windshield glass and then we recognize that unique, trademark color and shape.

Bud is first to break the silence. "Buster Brown. It's motherfucking UPS!"

With no time to lose, Lou starts barking orders again. "Let's try and get those last two billets loaded and get down off of this ridge before he comes back. At least we can get out of sight if we head for the bottom."

"I agree," says Don.

The last billets loaded, we move out of sight, shut our engines down, and listen while the UPS driver passes by on his way to his next stop. We wait for the gravel to quiet down before heading for the nearest lumber mill to trade the wood for money.

PART III

LAWYERS, JUDGES, AND MOBSTERS

While Don and I are busy with Bud and Lou, Larry Harshaw is talking with the attorney general's office in Harrisburg. Apparently they're very interested in our little investigation. They've also been getting complaints from landowners and foresters about timber theft. As the letter we received from their office states, they're "looking into putting together a task force or operation to look into the matter."

"Hey, Donny boy," I say to my partner as we make our way to Harrisburg for our scheduled meeting. "You suppose we're the task force or the operation for the investigation?"

"I don't know," he says. "Why couldn't we be the lookerinto-ers?"

"Possibly. But to me that conveys some sense of entitlement more suitable to a supervisory position."

"Well, we can't be the task force, because there are only two of us."

"That settles it," I say. "We are the operation."

Thinking about. Task force. Operation. Mother-fucking look into. Why don't they just grow a set? Just your typical politics in play.

////////////////////////////////

We have our first meeting with John and Paul from the attorney general's office at the Huntingdon regional headquarters. One is haughty, the other officious, and they strut around the office with the biggest gold badges I have ever seen clipped to their belts. The damn things look like bronc-rider championship buckles. Their official identification and side arms are similarly affixed, with the holster side out. The two of them sit in the conference room and listen as Don tells them everything we've discovered to date. We also share with them a little fact sheet with all the information we gathered:

Billet – A short section of a tree log, twenty to sixty-two inches in length with thirty-nine being the most in demand, minimum diameter ten inches.

End product – 90 percent are manufactured into 2" x 2" columns usually used to make stair railing parts. The leftover pieces are manufactured into flat dimension stock. The majority of this material is being exported to Europe, Japan, Taiwan, and Canada.

Raw material – Prime red oak is most in demand, plus small amounts of black cherry, white ash, and white oak.

Source of raw material – Anyone's wood lot, private, state, or federal, not under surveillance 24-7.

Area impacted – South to Elkins, West Virginia; north to southern New York; west to Ohio, and east into New Jersey.

In addition, we provided a list of ten current billet buyers, a price list from SupKo sawmill, and an advertising flier for K&F wood products.

"We've already been out working with one crew and got lucky and hooked up with a second," I tell them. "But anymore than that and the natives will start to get restless."

We propose the best way to gather evidence to prosecute current and dissuade future billet bandits is to set up a log yard and act as a buyer. "We would have to pay a little more than the other buyers," I say, "and if anyone asks how we're able to do that, I'll just tell them we only buy wood that we've already sold."

"We tell them we've invested a lot of time in making sure we have enough orders to keep the billets moving," adds Don.

John and Paul both seem excited about our plans, so we start to talk about the details. We try to cover all of the bases, sharing with them a list of things we'll need to pay for in order to pull this off: electricity, water, fuel, cameras, recorders, staff to run the mill, etc. We'll need a big saw too, but we'll never have to run it. We only need to be there to buy the billets, which we can then take somewhere and resell.

There are a lot of legal issues that we need guidance on. But these are questions we'll have to save for the attorney general's office, since they are supposed to be the experts.

"These guys are more pomp than circumstance," I say after our meeting. "If you and I set up that billet yard and start getting good information, the AG might come on over and run with it. But you and I are too invested to see that not everybody shares our work ethic and concern for the resource. After all, what do a couple of dead trees in Middle-Fuck Pennsylvania mean to his constituents anywhere else?"

The attorney general's office occupies floors fourteen, fifteen, and sixteen of Strawberry Square Tower—a collection of stores, shops, restaurants, and government offices in downtown Harrisburg. We find a parking garage that we can fit our truck into and then walk a couple of blocks to the lobby, where we are escorted up to the seventeenth floor. John and Paul meet us there and give us a quick tour of all three floors.

After that, we gather in what looks like a classroom with John, Paul, one inspector, and one attorney, and we pretty much repeat the report we gave back in Huntingdon, with one addition: Don and I had returned to Butch's log yard, and this time we brought along one of those handheld micro-cassette recorders and hid it beneath a map on the front seat between us.

Don reaches into his pocket and pulls out the recorder. As I relate our story, the room is getting strangely still, and a there's a growing look of perturbation on their faces.

"You guys have to hear this!" I say.

But as Don presses the play button, to a man they all cover their ears and shout, "No! Shut it off! Shut it off!"

And that, ladies and germs, is when Don and I learn that it's a felony to record someone's voice without their consent or a warrant (outside of the specific circumstances I described before). It's a mistake we never mistake again.

Every person in the room agrees we've made a good case. But there is no one there with the authority to authorize such a case. They do, however, have the authority swear us both in as special agents for the Bureau of Criminal Investigations in the Office of Attorney General. As far as we know, we are now the only officers in the Pennsylvania Game Commission to have this honor.

The Commonwealth of Pennsylvania established two types of wire intercepts. In a consensual intercept, one of the people in the conversation needs to know the conversation is being listened to and/or recorded and consents to same. Before an investigative or law enforcement officer records any communication under this law, their request must be reviewed by the state attorney general, deputy attorney general, district attorney, or deputy district attorney. If your case meets the probable cause standard, you will receive written permission to conduct your consensual intercept. There is so much paperwork, so many ass-kissing forms and signatures that need to be filled out in double-triplicate. The whole process for requesting a consensual recording requires such prodigious quantities of irreplaceable time that most officers forgo the wiretap/hidden-microphone option altogether.

As if the process was not prohibitive enough to reign in overzealous investigators, the Pennsylvania legislators, concerned about becoming the subject of a wiretap themselves, created a second, more restrictive section of the law stating that, if the intercept of communications was to take place in a private residence or business, it will be dubbed a nonconsensual wire.

Jack Thompson, the chief deputy assistant attorney general is the person designated to supervise our investigation and make certain I make the best use of the resources the Commonwealth has made available to us. He instructs me to work with the Pennsylvania Bureau of Criminal Investigations, which has some of the best investigative minds in the country. They are headquartered out of an abandoned PennDOT building that bears no significant marking or identifying feature but it is a hub of activity. Troopers and officers are constantly working on myriad investigations, reviewing photos, notes, recordings, and messages with bags, boxes, and cartons of evidence.

//////////////////////////////

I could have been a state trooper. Back in my senior year at Montana State University in Bozeman, where I was pursuing a B.S. in Fish and Wildlife Management, my mother sent me a newspaper clipping announcing the Pennsylvania Game Commission was conducting a written examination for the next training school class. I telephoned them and explained my situation, and they mailed the test to the Montana State Registrar's office, who administered the test by proxy and returned the results to the PGC. A week later I received notification I had passed the written portion of the selection process and I was awaiting notification of my date for the interview. Instead, I received a notice the nineteenth class of conservation officers was postponed for a year due to budgetary restrictions. Not one to wait around, after graduation from college I moved back to PA, took the state police exam, passed it, and received an invitation for an oral interview and a day of physical tests on strength and agility. I was twenty-four years old, six feet, four inches tall, and in the best condition of my life. I breezed through the physical challenges and moved into the oral interview. Each of the remaining candidates was interviewed by a panel of five.

"Fifty points is a perfect score," the captain yelled to the crowd as he handed each of us a folded piece of white paper. "Don't worry if it looks a little small. This is a tough interview panel. Anything around twenty and you're in."

I watched a couple guys open up their papers and show twenty, twenty-six, twenty-nine. Then I opened mine.

Forty-eight. I looked at it again and it still read forty-eight. I quickly stuffed it in my pocket. One of the others asked me how I did.

"I will see you in June," was all I said.

When I finished the four-hour drive home, my dad asked, "So, how did it go?"

"I made it."

"Guess who called?" he said.

I had no idea.

"The Game Commission. You report June fifth."

It was no contest. I didn't even think about the choice. I immediately sent a letter to the state police letting them know they could give my slot to the next man on the list. I was going to be a game warden.

//////////////////////////////

The attorney general thinks the next logical step in this case is to complete a request for an order authorizing interception of wire, electronic, or oral communications via operating a wiretap lawfully in the Commonwealth. A nonconsensual wire. Each time I turn that tape recorder on, I have to initiate it with a preamble giving my name, Class A certification number, case number, current date, and current time of day. When we are done recording,

I have to note the time of day again. Next, I have to complete a written narrative form briefly summarizing the events of the day, make four copies of the tapes, four copies of the forms, and deliver same to Thompson's expansive office.

I find Chief Deputy Assistant Atorney General Thompson to be a supercilious little man. He displays a pompous attitude toward me and tries to make sure I'm aware that if you don't have a law degree, you have no business in law enforcement. Despite that, John Thompson and his staff are practically effusive when I stroll into his office wearing my best, faded 501 LEVIs, my well-worn Justin lace-up boots, and my favorite Grateful Dead cutoff T-shirt.

"Our case is about to assume statewide notoriety," he says, looking like a man of some importance.

Giving it my best golly-gee-gosh expression, I smile. "Wow! Really?"

Thompson continues. "It seems that a short time ago a Pennsylvania Supreme Court ruling changed the interpretation of how we administer the Title 18, Chapter 57, Subsection B, as it relates to consensual and nonconsensual intercepts.

Thompson never missed the opportunity to remind me I was not as educated, sophisticated, or celebrated as he. Feigning profound interest, I respond, "Really?"

"What it means to you lay persons is—"

But I never hear the rest. I stop him short of his "Law for Dummies" lecture by finishing for him. "What it means is, as long as we are outside, the intercept was consensual and the order I had, approved by you, will allow me to record our conversation."

If he had read the affidavit of probable clause I had prepared for the warrant, as well as the one I had completed in order to get approval for the wiretap I am now operating, he might have seen and/or remembered that I have attended and completed the Class A certification in wiretapping and intercepting oral communications course, as is required by law. Not to mention the update class, which all Class A certification holders are obliged to attend following any significant legal or judicial changes. I know the law..

"But if you go inside his house," Thompson replies, "he has a greater expectation of privacy, and that requires us to obtain a non-consensual wiretap order."

I hesitate before adding, "Which requires the review and approval of the superior court judge in that district."

He nods. "We are the first case to test this landmark decision. I don't want to screw this up."

"I think that motherfucker set me up," I say to Woj. "He read all of my written reports. He knew we were going in and out of the house. There was no way Thompson was not aware of this decision. Our case was exactly what the AG was looking for when he read the report. It wasn't our choice to use a wire. In fact it was their fucking idea. I tried to talk them out of it. I told them we had all of that footage from the cameras, and ain't a picture worth a thousand words? But they wanted to have me apply for the wiretap." I'd never said anything to Woj, but I had to give Thompson credit for the maneuver.

I ask the troopers over at BCI how many times they've worn the wire. They say they would never wear a wire. That's what the confidential informants are for. Their covert officers don't even make a contact without a cover officer or team. That's reassuring.

//////////////////////////////

I gotta take a piss soon, I think as I pad silently toward the rear of my ice-, snow-, and road-salt-covered pickup truck.

Rossi is sitting behind the wheel, his sonorous voice easily audible as he engages the silver-haired man sitting in the shotgun seat—one of his many long-time friends, Sal Pietre.

Pietre is no stranger to the undercover operations of the Pennsylvania Game Commission. In fact, he was arrested and convicted along with numerous others ten years earlier as the result of a covert investigation conducted by PGC and US Fish and Wildlife Service agents. Pietre owned a bar where poachers sold deer, and he befriended the undercover US Fish and Wildlife agent who broke the case. Most recently he was arrested for kidnapping and terroristic threats. And it was Pietre who ended up telling the FBI who ordered the hit on the local district attorney.

Pietre is now seated on the passenger side of my truck, and I can hear him trying to convince Rossi that those two "Mike" guys could be undercover game wardens.

"They are sneaky fucking bastards," I hear Pietre say, as I stalk unobserved along the side of my pickup truck, the snow whispering under my boots.

"No fucking way, Sal. I know these guys. I checked them out."

"I hope you checked real fucking hard, Petey," Pietre replies, as I hear the glovebox snap open. "Those other guys had everything. Fake IDs, driver's licenses, hunting licenses, registrations…"

My blood goes cold. *Jesus fiddling Christ! What if I accidentally left something in there?* Then I take a breath and try to calm down. *Easy, Mike. You know the truck is clean. You checked it. You always check it. Then again, what if I missed something?*

I felt a cold stone rolling through my memory files to see if I had, in any way, been negligent. It could be so many things. Anything—a pay slip, my badge, a license plate number scribbled on the back of a grease-stained french-fry box, a laundry slip, a phone number; a fucking THANKS FOR 10 YEARS OF FUCKING SERVICE certificate my boss stuffed in my mail envelope. Everything might look like nothing to Rossi. With guys who have been down that block, however, guys like Pietre, anything could be everything.

When you make your living in covert operations, your cover is akin to the paint on a stealth bomber. If the paint is intact, you can fly in and drop your bombs undetected. But if that thin cloak flakes or fails, they can see you and blow you out of the fucking sky. If Pietre happens upon anything while ferreting about in my vehicle, anything that even hints I'm the law, it will be fight-or-flight time. Your stealth paint may hide you if you choose flight, but if you have to fight, it ain't worth diddly.

Easy, Mike. You can talk your way out of anything. My brain is whirling with possible scenarios and outcomes. *Steady. Just breathe.*

When their conversation slows and Pietre stops his search, I step up to the door.

Rossi flinches a little at my approach. "Oh, hey Mike. Sal here was trying to tell me you and the other Mike are game wardens. I told him if that's so, you were both dead—and I mean dead!"

As Rossi is talking, I notice Pietre is carrying a thirty-forty Krag bolt-action rifle. Pietre should have listened to his own instincts. As a convicted felon, that puts him in violation of his parole and adds another charge when the time comes.

///////////////////////////////

Things are beginning to heat up regarding our case, and I have to stop by Jim's office at PGC headquarters in Harrisburg. If it were business hours, I would enter via the warehouse and mailroom in the basement. Once in the building, I would borrow the phone from one of my buddies and buzz upstairs to let Jayne, Jim's administrative assistant, know I had come home. This would cause one of two things to happen: either Jayne would say, "I'll be down in a minute," which was good. Or she would say, "Jim needs to talk to you," which was not so good. Today turned out to be a not-so-good day.

When I walk into Jim's office, he leans back in his chair and his face broadens into a smile. "You've been busy," he says.

"You've been reading reports again," I reply.

"That's what they pay me for. I called over to the AG's office. You guys are getting into stolen ATVs, guns, merchandise, automatic weapons, and we need to get some help here. I also contacted the FBI and ATF."

I am biting my tongue, trying to keep my mouth shut, but it doesn't work. "That kind of help we don't need."

"Too late for that," he says. "The local PD already went to ATF. They and FBI have some guy named Pietre wearing a wire on Rossi."

"Sal, that son of a bitch!"

"What?"

"Never mind," I reply. "Keep going."

"That ain't all, Mikey. They have some shit-head doper or something wearing a wire for the DA and the local police department. Their subject is Rossi. You better watch your asses. They've been after Rossi for a long time, and they haven't been able to touch him."

The Eastern District of the Pennsylvania Superior Court oversees Carbon, Chester, Delaware, Lehigh, Monroe, Montgomery, Northampton, Philadelphia, Pike, and Wayne counties. Rossi lives and works in Carbon County. We, therefore, fall under the jurisdiction of the Eastern District based in Philadelphia. Thompson and I need to meet at that courthouse, but I can't risk being seen with him. So rather than ride over to Philadelphia from

Harrisburg together, I tell Thompson I have other business in the area and I'll meet him in front of the courthouse at zero eight thirty hours. Our appointment with the superior court judge is for zero nine-hundred.

I drive around the block twice before giving in to the reality that I will not be able to park anywhere convenient without getting towed and/or cited. There is this whole cable network series about the Philadelphia Parking Authority enforcement officers and the job they do every day. I don't want to get on the wrong side of those men and women.

Not wanting to fuck this up, I pull into one of the metered spots that requires a quarter every fifteen minutes. I decide I don't need my badge, since Thompson will have enough badges for the both of us. I toss mine up on the dashboard, lock my truck, and head to the court hoping I'm not going to be watching myself on an episode of *Parking Wars.*

"Good morning, Counselor," I say, smiling. "Beautiful day!"

"Yes it is," he replies. "And I am glad you are early. I want to go over some things."

For the umpteenth time I am lectured about the respect and admiration the judges expect at this level. I dare not speak to the judge unless he asks me to, and even then I'm to make sure to check with him if I have any questions. Just answer the judge's question, he instructs me. Don't elaborate. "These are very important people. They don't have the time to deal with or consider your opinion."

"Hey," I say, "of the people, by the people, for the people, right?"

Our footfalls echo as we walk down the polished marble floor to the courtroom. The Superior Court judge, robes and all, is seated on the far side of a large table with two chairs, the arms tucked under the near side of the table. There is also a stenographer typing to our left. Immediately to our right is the bench he normally occupies. The judge is looking very thoughtful as we approach the table.

Just then recognition begins to spread across his face, and he laughs loudly, saying, "Hey, Michael, how the fuck are you? You tell your boss he still owes me fucking money."

Relieved, I tell him I will absolutely convey his concerns. "But I think Your Honor might be throwing his water bucket down a dry well."

Again, he laughs. "Well, come on over here and show me what we've got."

The first time I met Matt Perkins he was the District

Attorney in Cumberland County, Pennsylvania. The subject of the investigation at the time was one Gino Lombardi, a toady of suspected drug dealer Rick Faust. Faust was an airline pilot for US Air. According to authorities, he use to smuggle the dope in his pilot's luggage to avoid the scrutiny of the police who inspect the luggage and bags of the passengers. Exotic felines were in vogue, and the local drug lords decided Lombardi was the man who could supply them. I contacted Lombardi and asked him what he could get for me. I had a Carlisle address and phone number; Lombardi lived in Pittsburgh.

"I told him I was on one of the construction crews working on I-81." I am bringing Jim up to speed on the Lombardi case. "He claims he has a black leopard cub for sale. So I agreed to give him $2,100 for the cat."

"Where is the deal going down?"

"Somewhere between here and the Steel City."

"Think you can get him to come over here?"

"Where to?"

"Anywhere in Cumberland County," says Jim. "District Attorney Matt Perkins is a good friend and a good man."

"I will make it happen," I reply, as I handed him the request for funds to purchase evidence. "As soon as you give me 2,100 American dollars." And that's how I met then District Attorney, now Judge Perkins.

I make arrangements to meet with Lombardi at the intersection of Interstate 81 and State Route 233. The road signs declare this as Exit 37, Newville. The road signs also indicate there is a Park-and-Ride lot at this exit. A tumult of road construction surrounds the immediate area. I am sitting on the tailgate of my pickup with my lunch-sized cooler open, eating at my sandwich, when Lombardi pulls up beside me and climbs out of his car. I am wearing a fluorescent orange tank top, a pair of threadbare Carhartt canvas work pants, and scuffed, concrete-splashed Dunham boots. The final prop in my make-believe world is an orange-colored, well-worn plastic hard hat sitting on the tailgate next to my equally worn, eight-quart cooler.

I place my sandwich back into my cooler and stand up. "Gino?" I ask.

"Yeah. You Mike?"

"The last time I checked I was."

Lombardi acts like he doesn't even hear me. Obviously, my attempts at humor are going to be wasted on this guy. So, we just get right down to business.

Lombardi opens the rear side door of his SUV, reaches inside and comes out holding a small pet carrier. He walks over and sets the carrier on my tailgate. I couldn't have asked him to place it in a better position. I fired up the camera and recorder just as he arrived.

"Here she is," says Lombardi, reaching into the pet carrier and pulling out a black jaguar cub that looks malnourished, dehydrated, and tired. Instead of a playful, curious, energetic ball of claws, eyes, and teeth, she is lethargic and non-responsive. The little cub needs help, and fast.

"She looks a little thin for...what'd you say she is, six weeks old?" I am trying not to lose my temper. I have to remember the camera is on, and it could be detrimental to my case if I'm caught on film smacking the shit out of this asshole.

"The vet has her medicine in this bottle," Lombardi says, handing me a four-ounce bottle with an eyedropper screwed into the top. "Give her one eyedropper full, twice a day."

I don't bother asking him what the medicine is supposed to be curing. The first thing this jaguar needs is an IV for fluid to treat the dehydration and some proper formula. This little girl should still be living on her momma's milk.

"I have a girl who wants a cat." I say. "I wanted to get her something different, and, I mean, you just brought me a jaguar. How fucking cool is that?"

"I've been working on getting a snow leopard, too," he replies. "Might come through in a few weeks."

"A snow leopard! I am definitely into that."

"Good. I'll call you in a couple of weeks."

"Oh, shit. I got so excited about the cat I almost forgot to pay you for her." I pull a roll of 100-dollar bills out of my pocket. "You said $2,100, and I gave you a $500 deposit, so I owe you $1,600." I count out sixteen 100-dollar bills onto my open tailgate right in front of the lens, which is hidden inside a toolbox. Then Lombardi and I shake hands and part ways.

Now it's time to try and save this leopard. That's right, I said *leopard*. What Mr. Lombardi is representing to be a threatened jaguar is actually an endangered leopard, which upgrades his crime to federal and state felonies.

It is a little before one in the afternoon and I need to contact Jim Beard for help. We are still in the era before cell phones, remember. Two years down the road, I'll just pick up my cell phone, press a button, and be speaking with Jim in seconds. At this time, though, I have to find a phone booth, dial an eleven-digit number, and then enter a sixteen-digit credit card number, all the time hoping I don't get one number wrong. Because if I do, I'll have to hang up and begin again from the start. But as it turns out, I have to go past Jim's office to get to where I am going anyway, so I just decide to just stop in.

Twenty minutes later I slip into the boss's office. He's

on the phone, so he waves me in and I comply. I never have a problem understanding what Jim has to say. Whether in person or via telephone, his voice always prevails.

"Well, he's so dumb he's happy," he says into the receiver. Jim certainly has a unique way of putting things. "All right." Pause. "Well, I have to go." Pause. "Yeah, Mikey just walked in." Another pause. "All right. Yeah, I'll call you." He pushes the end-call button on his phone, mumbling, "fucking dip shit," before turning to me.

I don't bother asking who the "dip shit" is. I just want to get out of there. "I need your help," I say. "What is the name of that rehabber in Ono?"

Jim still looks puzzled, so I give him some context. "I bought that jaguar, which is really a leopard, and it doesn't look so well."

"What's wrong with him?"

"First off, he is a she, and she is at dehydrated and malnourished."

Jim still has that I-still-don't-know-what-the-fuck-you-are-talking-about look upon his face.

I continue. "You and I discussed what we were going to do with a baby jaguar, if I indeed bought one."At last I see recognition begin to dawn under that furrowed brow.

"Do you mean Juanita, the wildlife rehabilitation permittee?" he says. "Juanita Warner?"

"Finally!"

A wildlife rehabilitation permit allows holders to possess, treat, and otherwise care for wild animals who are injured or sick. Their ultimate goal is to treat the animal until it is capable of living on its own and can be returned to the wild. Sometimes an animal cannot be released, in which case they are asked to care for an animal until a better home for it can be found.

Juanita is happy to care for our endangered leopard. When she examines the poor creature, she says that if we hadn't brought it in, it would've most likely been dead in two days.

//////////////////////////////

"The law provides a manner to recoup your $2,100," Matt Perkins says to me in his office in Carlisle. "It is called restitution. Both federal and state statutes have provisions that require the guilty to pay all fines and costs of prosecution."

"Does that mean Lombardi has to buy my lunch?" I ask, smiling. "I mean, it was only a PB&J, but hey, money is money. I've even documented it on film."

Perkins laughs. "If it were up to me, he would have to buy your gas and pay your salary."

"Having him pay my salary is not much of

a penalty."

Perkins changes gears. "What do you want to do with Mr. Lombardi?"

"Well, he claims he is working on getting a snow leopard. But I think that it's all bullshit. He has me figured for a rube. There is no way this loser is going to get his mitts on one of the most critically endangered cats on this planet."

"Why would he tell you that he can get one?"

"One word:" I reply, "deposit. He knows I have the money because I already paid a deposit once. Then he watched me pull over $3,000 out of the pocket of my work pants. He knows I am not concerned about writing checks and mailing them. He thinks that I trust him."

"Why would he think you trust him? He sold you a dead cat."

"Mostly dead. But Judge Perkins—"

He interrupts me. "Not yet. I have an election to win."

"OK, your future Honor," I say. "Lombardi thinks… no, he *knows* I trust him. I'm too stupid not to. He figures I can't go to the cops because, by testifying, I would be incriminating myself. And according to the stripper that tipped me off, that is his M.O. He did the same thing to her."

Perkins furrows his brow. "Stripper? What stripper?"

"Long story."

"I'm willing to bet he will take my next deposit and disappear."

And he does. Lombardi cashes check No. 387 for $1,500 as a deposit on a snow leopard and never answers his phone after cashing the check.

The next time I see (still District Attorney) Perkins I am handing him the probable cause affidavit I recently finished for the arrest warrant for Gino Lombardi. It includes a violation of the Endangered Species Act; Title 18, Pa Crimes Code felony theft by deception, theft by unlawful disposition of funds received; and Title 34, Pa Game and Wildlife Code, possession or sale of threatened or endangered species. Perkins could assign the case over to one of his assistant DAs, but he handles the case from the arraignment through the preliminary hearing.

We are scheduled for trial when Perkins receives a phone call from Sandra Miller, US Attorney from the western district of Pennsylvania. Miller says they have an open case on Rick Faust, and their information disclosed a close association between Faust and Gino Lombardi. In order to encourage Lombardi to cooperate with them, they need some leverage. As of this date, they'd found nothing. If Lombardi had been arrested for a crime that would result in a large enough fine or significant jail time, the US Attorney's office could offer to reduce or eliminate his sentence in exchange for his testimony against Faust. Since we are waiting for defense to offer some sort of plea bargain proposal, it would be the perfect time to make a deal with Lombardi.

Perkins did not believe this was going to trial anyway. "Ninety-five percent of our cases are settled out of court," he says.

"I did not know it was that high," I reply.

"Besides," Perkins continues, "counsel for the defense knows his client is fucked. The testimony is all first-hand. You are such a credible witness, he has nothing to attack."

There is one problem with the US Attorney's plan: it's not her case. She cannot make any deals with Lombardi or his attorney unless Perkins drops his case first.

Perkins's intercom buzzes and the voice of his assistant tells him US Attorney Sandra Miller is on line two. Immediately, the phone on his desk rings into life, and he snaps up the receiver. "Matt Perkins." He listens for a minute then says, "Yes, I am very familiar with the case. I am prosecuting it."

I can hear the tone of Miller's voice, but not what she's saying.

"I do not have any problem with handing the case over to you," Perkins continues, "but I need to talk to the investigating officer first. Yes, ma'am. No, ma'am. Yes, ma'am. I will get back to you as soon as I talk with the officer. I understand that you do not work that way. Yes, I know this is *your* jurisdiction, but this is *my* county, and local rules apply. No, I work for the citizens of Cumberland County. You have yourself a nice day also. Goodbye." With that, Perkins presses the end call button several times and waits for the safety of the dial tone before placing the handset back in its cradle. "Fucking bitch."

"I appreciate the sentiment," I say, "but you don't want to poke that bear with my stick. I've done my job, thanks to your help. If Miller wants to gamble with our part to snare a bigger prize, then I wish her the best. I don't have a dog in that fight."

////////////////////////////

The next time I see Perkins is in the courtroom, where I am appearing before him with an affidavit of probable cause, showing why I should be permitted to use a nonconsensual wiretap to investigate Peter Rossi. He's been voted into office, and Superior Court Judge Matt Perkins reads my affidavit and signs his approval.

Thompson, from the time we walk in until we are back

outside in the warm sunlight, never says a word. Once we're outside, he says, "Why didn't you tell me you knew the judge?"

"Well," I say, "you never asked."

After all of the lawyers, judges, investigators, and agents work to get the wiretap approved, we finally get permission to record the voice of Peter Rossi.

//////////////////////////////

Far from home and with Rossi in the back of my mind, I pull into Baxter Hunting Lodge, way up in Baxter, Maine, a little after 6 p.m.

I can hear hounds baying as we drive up. I get out of my truck and give the hounds my best version of a sergeant bawling out his conscripts for a major infraction. It works, and the dogs fall silent.

I walk through the door of the lodge into the social area, where the hunters can relax, pore through outdated hunting magazines, and swap lies. Standing in the common area is outfitter Ryan Murphy and one of his guides, North Carolina's own John Sanders, aka "Junkyard Dog," along with five clients all covered in new camouflage shirts, pants, and boots. I'd met both Sanders and Murphy a few months back. Sanders was one of 43 people arrested in "Operation Smokey"—a three-year, joint operation of the US Fish and Wildlife Service, the National Park Service, the US Marshall Service, the Tennessee Bureau of Investigation, and wildlife agencies in Tennessee, North Carolina, and Georgia. Agents were able to purchase 266 bear gallbladders, which is considered a potent aphrodisiac in China, along with 385 bear claws, 77 bear feet, four bear heads, nine bear hides, and one live bear cub. Of the 43 indicted, 25 were from North Carolina, including Sanders; nine from Tennessee, and one from Georgia. Murphy's uncle was also one of the arrests in North Carolina.

Today, the Maine Warden Service wants to determine if Murphy is guiding raft trips without the required guide license. It's up to me to get my foot in the door and try to make Murphy more comfortable. I've stopped by a few times now, and I know Murphy by name.

"Hey, Ryan," I begin. "I am in no hurry to get back to Pennsylvania. What would you charge me to stay a couple nights? There's a pizza shop back in town, so I can buy own meals."

"Sure," Murphy replies, "if you don't mind bunking with Junkyard. He snores, so don't say I didn't warn you."

"I don't need a bunk," I say. "I always sleep in the bed of my pickup."

I end up spending two nights with Ryan Murphy and

Junkyard Dog, then head south. Along the way I stop outside of Portland to check in with Sergeant Wilcox. I tell him I don't think Murphy is in the rafting business or, if he was, he isn't any longer. "One of his guides was there," I say. "John Sanders is his name. Calls himself Junkyard Dog. I spent a day riding around with them and checking and replenishing Murphy's bear bait sites. He was working off a topographic marking, where all of his bait sites were located. I videoed that map." I hand the sergeant the tape and continue. "He also had some notes he was poring over, something having to do with cow and bull-moose permits. He had a bunch of permit numbers and license numbers he had been working on. I figured it looked like something you guys might be interested in seeing, so I took some footage of that too." It was my opinion Murphy is having Maine residents, who were guaranteed bull moose permits, hunt with his clients who were nonresidents and had to be drawn for a license. Set up well, it would be very difficult to prove who actually shot the bull.

"You still up for the fall bear hunt?" Wilcox asks.

"Sure. I thought it went well," I reply. "I earned his trust by hanging around swapping lies for a couple of nights."

Wilcox smiles. "The local officer is going to love that map. I will get to work on the moose tag stuff." Then he stands to shake my hand. "We will see you in a few months,

Mike. Have a safe trip home."

//////////////////////////////

That's how, four months later, I find myself standing in front of Ryan Murphy and guests, 600 miles from my home.

"Let's get you boys checked in," says Murphy. "First I need to see your hunting license."

"Here you go," I say, digging mine out of my wallet and handing it to him.

"Looks good, Mr. Duncan," he says, smiling. Then he turns to Dave, and I watch in abject horror as Dave hands Murphy all four copies of his Maine nonresident hunting license: his hunter's copy, the selling agent's copy, the Maine Warden Service copy, and the file copy.

Murphy looks at all four copies and then turns to me, fuming. "What the fuck?!"

Oh, I think, *this is not going to be good.* My adrenal glands go straight to DEFCON five, and I can hear my heartbeat pounding inside my head like the sound of a thousand troops marching across an old wooden bridge. My auditory and visual senses magnify, and my breath rate doubles as the primordial instinct of fight or flight takes over. I knew this was a bad fucking idea.

This is one of the most stressful situations for a covert officer. You have to live with these people 24-7, and your cover had better be bulletproof. You better be able to discuss your assumed identity. If you don't have your story straight every time you tell it, you could be in a heap of trouble. You need to choose your identity carefully.

I suggest to all new special investigators that they keep their first name. It is what you have always called yourself and what you have always responded to. When the heat is on and the stress is high, it is one less thing you can get wrong. I also prefer to keep the first letter of my last name the same, in case you forget who you are signing for, on duty and off. I chose my current ID, "Mike Duncan," because it's the last name of the game commission's current executive director. It is also the name of the marshal in *High Plains Drifter* who gets whipped to death, prompting Clint Eastwood to ride back into town to avenge him.

You have to be ready for any question they throw at you. Where are you from? Where do you live now? What a coincidence! I live there! Where are you in relation to a certain landmark or structure? Where did you go to school? College? What is your wife's name? Any children? What are their names? How old are they? Where do you work? For how long? What breed of dog do you have? You should expect and prepare to hear the same questions at another time, and damn well better have the same answers. If you are working with a partner, depending on the story you are telling, she or he might have to know the answers to those same questions and more. Just as you may have to know the answers to those questions about your partner. And you better make damn certain nothing on your person has anything that could blow your cover.

Let me explain. It all started on a cool, cloudy Maine morning when I pulled my pickup into Dave Malone's driveway. The Maine Warden Service had requested assistance investigating Ryan Murphy. My partner on this job is Maine Warden Dave Malone. I don't ask the warden service why they decide to send one of their officers along for the ride. It doesn't really matter. The decision has been made. It's their case and their money. I have some trepidations, but I march on.

Dave's home is situated in one of hundreds of small fishing towns along Maine's rocky coast, were there are more lobster boats than automobiles. We both knew we didn't have much time, so we made our introductions and got right to work.

"OK, David," I began, "first and most important, let's make sure we don't have anything we are not supposed to have. I never carry or bring my badge or credentials into the arena. In fact, I am going to leave my personal wallet right here and pick it back up whenever we get done."

"What about if I bring it but keep it hidden?" he asked.

"You can't guard your luggage the whole time we're there. I fully expect them to search the truck, so you cannot stash it there. And if you carry it around all of the time, someone is liable to ask you to see it. You could lose it or drop it or accidentally pull it out because you have done this all of your life and it is ingrained in your muscle memory.

"I guess you're right."

"The only thing your ID is going to do is get you in trouble." I said, thinking, *well, at least he isn't mule-headed.*

We checked our bags again for any condemning pieces of paper, like luggage tags with the wrong name on them. We also we make certain we haven't packed any GAME WARDENS DO IT ALL NIGHT T-shirts. Then we check to make sure we both have our bear-killing guns and plenty of bear-killing ammo. Last but not least, I ask Dave if he has his bear license.

"Thank God you asked," he replies. "I darn near forgot it." He hurries upstairs to his office, where I hear paper rustling and then the distinct sound of a typewriter pounding its keys on paper.

"What are you doing up there, Officer Malone?"

"I'm..." he says, hesitates, and then continues, "...

Sergeant Wilcox gave me a couple of blanks."

"Blanks? Blank what's?"

"Blank hunting licenses. I am just filling my covert name and address in the right spots."

"Dave, do you check a lot of hunting licenses when you're out in the field?"

"Of course," he replies. "It's one of our primary responsibilities as—"

"Primary responsibility as an officer, blah, blah, blah," I cut him off. "Look, I didn't go to the same schools as you did but I got the same training. I am well aware of the reasons officers check hunting licenses. My question for you now is, how many licenses have you checked that have been completed with an old-fashioned typewriter?" I can't see his face, but I don't have to. In my mind I see him sitting in his game warden's office chair holding his new, nonresident bear license in his hand and thinking, *"This is a lot more complicated than I anticipated."* I can hear the steps squeaking as he comes back down.

"Not all of our license dealers have the computer and automated printers," he says. "Some of them don't even have phones."

"I know. But if old Maynard has no printer, is he likely to have a typewriter?"

Dave thinks for a moment and then replies, "No, I

guess not."

"I suggest you get another blank license. By the way, is your wife home?"

"Yeah. Why?"

"Good, have her fill out the license with the information you want, then *you* sign it. At least the handwriting won't match either of us. We can work on where you bought it on the drive up."

"OK," he replies. "Sounds good."

"Speaking of the drive up," I continue, "we better get moving soon. As John Wayne said in *The Cowboys,* we're burnin' daylight."

Soon we are northbound on Interstate 95, and that's when I have an epiphany of sorts. "I don't know why I didn't think of this earlier," I say.

"What's that?"

"Your license."

"What about it?"

"You boldly walk on in like the nonresidents we are—well, at least I am—and then buy a nonresident Maine bear license. It'll cost you a little over a hundred bucks, but it would be better for us not to worry about Murphy questioning the validity of the license. Besides, the money you give for the license goes back to the agency." The look on Dave's face and the sag in his shoulders tells me everything I needed to know. "You are supposed to be from Massachusetts. You don't have a covert driver's license from the state of Massachusetts, do you?"

He shakes his head no in reply. Dave Malone is a smart man and a quick learner. But what you learn when you're actually doing undercover work is nothing like what you see in the movies.

"Jesus, Mary, and Joseph, Dave! Every time we overcome an obstacle your hierarchy casts another one before us."

//////////////////////////////

"That stupid bitch!" I shout, slamming my right fist into the palm of my left hand. "I knew she had something fucked up, that dumb gash!" I have all of them looking at me as I try to talk my way out of another clusterfuck. "So…we go into LL Bean…" I am making all of this up as I speak. Entirely impromptu. Trying to remember something that never really happened. "…and we go over to the counter advertising license sales…" Meanwhile, I am reliving in my mind a scene that I never even lived. My brain is editing my mouth. *Say her hair is short. No! She had long hair. Describing her makes your story seem more credible and lowers the number of women who could have handled the transaction. Keep her as generic as possible. It could have been any female employee.*

It had to be a woman. These rednecks don't believe women should be allowed to drive or vote. Only a woman could fuck up something as simple as this. "She told us the computers were down, and that she'd have to process our licenses by hand. She said she was new and never did one manually before."

"That's the problem with kids these days," says one of the hunting guests. "If they can't do it on a computer, they can't do it at all. All she learned how to do was take your driver's license and slide it through that little slot on the computer. The machine does the rest, prints out everything you need, including the bill."

I am relieved to see some of the older clients nodding their heads in understanding. "Now I am standing in L.L.Bean after having to drive fourteen hours, the last four of which I have a passenger I recently met, whose farts smell like something crawled up inside of him and died. I was fucking pissed, and the madder I got, the louder I complained, and the more the new dipshit came unglued. Her world was unraveling because the fucking computer locked up." I turn to Dave. "That reminds me, I saw her using your driver's license to fill out your hunting license, but I never saw her return it to you. I meant to ask you before we left Bean's, but I got pissed off and forgot it." In my mind I'm thinking, c'mon, Dave, get back in the game—the undercover game! Finally, he does.

Immediately Dave fusses around in his pockets, searching for a license he never had. "I can't find it. Damnit! I must have left it back there."

At this point Murphy says, "Look, I know a lot of people at L.L.Bean. I'll call them and find out what the fuck is going on down there."

It's a Donald Trump-like lie. A bluff that I decide to call. "Hell, Ryan, there ain't a phone within forty miles of here. You'd just be wasting your time. Besides, they processed the license by hand so they wouldn't have anything in their records until the computers came back on, and then they'd have to enter his license information."

Murphy's look of cold, hard anger begins to melt into a look of skepticism as I keep throwing out everything I can, hoping he will latch on to something.

"Think about it," I continue, "since Boy Wonder here walked away with all four copies of the license, L.L.Bean has nothing to enter when the computers come back on. Even if you could get through to the Rhodes scholar who fucked all this up, it doesn't help anything." I can see now that Murphy is taking my story, hook, line, and sinker. "Now, I can understand if you're upset about me surprising you with an unexpected client. But man, Ryan, calling you this time of year is impossible. I figured you could use the extra fifteen-hundred for the hunt." The mention of cold, hard cash has its intended purpose. Murphy had forgotten all about the money side of the game. The more someone pays you, the more credible their story becomes.

Just then Murphy thinks he's caught me in a lie. "Wait a second. How do you end up taking someone to Maine you just met?"

Again, I have to be quick on my feet. "Well, my sister is always talking about how much I love to hunt. And she knew Dave here loved to hunt too. He's her brother-in-law, her husbands's little brother. So she talked me into picking him up on the way through."

Murphy looks wary. "How do you not meet your sister's brother-in-law at your sister's wedding?"

This guy is good, I think. "Oh, he was there, all right, but my sister had decided to have her wedding the same week as my weeklong mountain lion hunt in Montana." Then, cracking a smile, I add, "She might have another wedding, but I might never get another chance at a cougar in Montana." Never before have I spoken for so long and so loudly. I feel as if I have to remonstrate for the lives of two men, one being yours truly. "Man, I need a beer after all of this bullshit."

"The closest bar is back in Medway," says Murphy. Apparently he bought my story. "About forty miles or so."

"Yeah," says Dave, "we came through Medway on our

way up here."

"Take eleven south when you come into Baxter..." Murphy begins.

"I know the way," I say. "Anybody else want anything? Going once...going twice...no sale?" After that we step outside, and I pull the door shut behind us.

As we walk toward my truck, Dave asks where we're going.

"To get beer," I say.

He looks stunned. "Wait a minute, we are *not* going back in *there*, are we?"

"Oh, yes we are."

"No, Mike. You can't. You're fucking crazy!"

I turn and look him in the eye. "Look, if we run now, they are going to know we are game wardens. But if we go back, they'll think there is no way we are. We'd have to be the craziest motherfucking wardens to ever carry a fucking gun and a badge. Personally, I like our odds."

"You are the craziest motherfucker, period, Mike, badge or not. There is no fucking way man. Think about it!"

"I have thought about it, Dave. I am going to the bar to get some beer. You are going to call your sergeant or whoever is handling this case and tell them to get somebody into L.L.Bean and have them verify our story, just in case Murphy calls. Understand?"

"Yeah, I think so."

"No, Dave, don't think—do! Also, tell them to have somebody fly over Murphy's camp in two days. My truck is the only pickup with a white cap on it. If we're OK, there will be a dark grey wool army blanket spread out on the cap. The forecast is calling for sunshine and warm weather all week. It will not be unusual for me to get some fresh air and sunshine on my bedding. I doubt any of them can see it from the ground, it's too high."

Dave is listening intently.

"On the other hand, if there isn't any blanket, we are in trouble and need assistance. Have them send in a team to arrest you and me. Tell them the story is that, while I was returning home from my visit earlier this year, I robbed a sporting goods store just below Portland. Say I took a few handguns and a book of Maine hunting licenses, two of which you and I are currently in possession of. You got all that?"

"Yes, sir."

"Repeat it back to me." And Dave does, almost verbatim. I guess being number one in his class comes in handy after all. The whole flying-over thing is just an attempt to boost Dave's confidence. If our cover is blown, we'll most likely be bear bait before the arrest team gets to us.

Dave has calmed considerably by the time we pull into the yard beside the Baxter Hunting Lodge. Along the way back, I'd warned him to not say a word unless someone asked him a direct question. "They'll most likely put some pressure on me," I say, "since I was doing all of the lying last time. Stick with the we-recently-met-and-don't-know-a-thing-about-each-other story, and you'll be fine."

"The first time we laid eyes on each other was at the truck stop north of Worcester," he says.

"That's right. And I didn't talk much because I was pissed off, especially after the L.L.Bean fiasco."

"Right. And we will go back to L.L.Bean and get my driver's license on the way back home."

"Today's word of the day is deny," I continue. "Deny, deny, deny! If they say they know you're a game warden, you tell them flat out they are wrong. No matter what they say or do—you keep denying! I don't care if they have your ID, your badge, and a fucking picture of you wearing that red, Dudley Do-Right, Canadian Mounty coat on your graduation day. You just say, THAT AIN'T ME! Got it?"

"Got it."

"Good."

Before going inside, we stand at the front of my truck. I'm not concerned about being overheard. Luckily our arrival has rallied the hounds to full cry, overwhelming any competing sound waves.

"Get a good night's sleep," I tell Dave. "Murphy won't fuck with us anymore tonight. It's too late. He has all night to think about it. I expect he'll start playing the game tomorrow."

Dave is carrying his rifle, his bag, and a pair of those white lobsterman boots you only see on lobster boats. Dumb fucker. He is supposed to be from Massachusetts. But I don't want to give him anything else to worry about tonight, so I just turn and head for the back of my pickup.

"Hey," he says, "where are you going?"

"My friend, I have stayed in enough hunting camps to learn that the man who snores the loudest, falls asleep the fastest." Then, climbing into the bed of the truck, and before closing the cap door, I yell, "Quiet now! That's enough!" in a language only a hound can understand. And with that the hounds fall blessedly silent.

As I walk into the dining room early the next morning, I exchange greetings with four men all dressed in the latest real-tree camo pattern.

"Mornin'," I say, "I'm Mike, Mike Duncan." I can tell which one of them is number one in the pecking order. The other three sit patiently while he finishes chewing the piece of bacon in his mouth.

"I'm Jimmy," says the lead dog. "This one here is Sal,

and across from me is Bobbie and Mark. Call him Marko. Unless you're mad at him, that is. Then feel free to call him whatever you want."

That brings a much-needed laugh out of me. These guys look and sound like they just crossed the Brooklyn Bridge for the first time yesterday!

"Where were you last night?" Sal asks me.

"I slept in the back of my truck."

"Slept in the back of his truck," both Marko and Bobbie repeat in unison, laughing.

"In the back of his fucking truck," echoes Sal. "You hear that, Jimmy?"

"I heard you pull in," replies DeMarco, "because all of those goddamned dogs started barking."

"We thought they were gonna bark all fucking night," adds Sal, "but you yelled and they shut right the fuck up. You and Ryan are the only ones they listen to. You must be one of those redneck hillbillies they have down there in Pennsylvania."

We all laugh, then Bobbie chimes in. "You got the ponytail, the pickup truck, even the fucking gun racks. You're a country boy, all right."

And so goes my first encounter with a member of the Gambino family—one of John Gotti's caporegime, Jimmy DeMarco, along with three of his soldiers. DeMarco made his money selling seafood in the longtime mob-associated Fulton Fish Market.

Just then Murphy comes in from the kitchen, where he's been talking with our cook and most likely listening to our conversation. Shortly after, Dave walks in talking with the last two clients, Don and Brad from Paramus, New Jersey, and everybody is introduced to everybody else.

After breakfast, as we ease off our dining chairs, Don tells Murphy, "That was a fine breakfast. Give the cook or chef or whatever they are called now, our compliments."

We step outside, out of the smell of bacon and black coffee, and into the smell of golden rod and pitch pine.

"Go get your guns and gear, boys," says Murphy. "We're going bear hunting."

Murphy has an old Chevy Suburban, flat brown in color, as well as a white, extended-cab Ford pickup flatbed with a stack of dog boxes on the back up against the cab. The dogs know something is about to happen. I follow Murphy over to the kennels, where he grabs Duchess, an old grey Plott hound. He clips on her lead and hands it to me. She's a mellow old girl, probably almost deaf from listening to those foolish black-and-tans make a ruckus at all hours.

"She has the best nose of them all," says Murphy, as he struggles to contain two rambunctious black-and-tan hounds. "Once she gets on a trail, she never gets fooled and never quits." Then he leads the dogs to the truck, where they scramble aboard and are stuffed into their boxes. I scoop up the old Plott and set her on the truck bed. "She's a runner, too," Murphy says, as he opens the door to her dog box. She walks in like royalty, turning to face out, and flops to the straw in the bottom of the box.

By now the others have all gathered around. Murphy turns to me. "You gonna get your gun, Mike?"

At that moment I look over at Dave Malone in his eastern Maine lobsterman boots, carrying a semi-automatic rifle. I should have noticed that when we packed, but I'd been a little distracted at the time. Semi-automatic rifles are legal in Maine, but Dave is supposed to be from Massachusetts, where they are decidedly not. I have to pull my shit together right fucking now.

"Nah, Ryan," I say. "I count eight hunters. You might be good, but I don't think you can round up eight bear in one day. I shot one already a couple of years ago out in Montana." I am speaking to the whole group now. "I'll give the Jersey boys and Jimmy's crew first chance."

DeMarco gives me a nod of approval.

"All right," says Murphy. "Jimmy, you drive the Suburban. Dave, Don, and Brad, you guys get in with Jimmy, Sal, Mark, and Bobbie." Then he turns to me. "Mike, you look like you can help handle the dogs. You ride with me."

As soon as our tires hit the hard road, Murphy goes to work with a barrage of questions. "What's your friend's name again?"

"Who," I say, "Dave?"

"Dave, that's it. Dave. And what's his last name?"

I know what it is, of course. Dave and I had gone over it a hundred times. But Murphy wants to play the game. *OK, Murphy, I'm your huckleberry*, I think, channeling my inner Doc Holiday. *That's just my game.* "I don't know," I say. "Just met him yesterday."

"Isn't his brother married to your sister?

"Boy, I hope so. Otherwise, Momma is gonna be pissed off because they're living in sin."

Murphy keeps pressing. "So you don't know your sister's last name?"

"I never said that."

"So, you do know his last name?"

"I didn't say that, either."

"But you do know your sister's last name?"

"Yes." Never answer more questions than you are asked.

"So, what is it?"

"What?"

"Your sister's last name! Christ."

"Her last name is Duncan," I reply. "She's one of those

uppity bitches who insists on keeping her maiden name. That's Duncan, like the doughnuts, only spelled different. D-U-N-C-A-N, in case that is one of your questions." By this point I am fed up with the inquisition. "How about it, Ryan? Michael Duncan, born March fifth, 1960, eight pounds, ten ounces, to Mike Duncan and Helen Duncan. Not Mike D-U-N-C-A-N SENIOR, though. Mike is his given name. The name that's on his fucking birth certificate. Current address, Box 1075, Carlisle, P-A. You ever think about that, Ryan? Why they call it P-A? No, of course not. You live up in M-E. Except they don't call it Mmmmm-Eeeeeee. In fact, the Commonwealth of Pennsylvania is the only state that is referred to in such a casual manner. I know you're thinking D-C, as in Washington, D.C. But Washington, D.C., is not a state—it is a DISTRICT. They don't even have representation in Congress. You never hear Hollywood, C-A, Denver, C-O, or Winnemucca, N-V. Why is that, Ryan? Trying to figure that out has driven me crazy, Ryan. Cuckoo, baby. So let's clear the air here. What is it that has you playing twenty goddamn questions with me? You think I'm a fucking game warden? Well…I AM!"

As I am saying all this, I pull my wallet out of my pocket and flash it open, revealing my driver's license and my Giant Eagle discount FuelPerks card. Murphy damn near wrecks the truck. I don't usually go off rail like this, but seeing Dave the lobsterman outfit with his thirty-caliber, semi-automatic rifle from Massa-two-shits was all I can stand, and I can't stands no more. Desperate times call for desperate measures.

"You know, Ryan," I continue, "I really don't know shit about Dave. Don't know if he's a Republican or Democrat. Don't know if he is a genus or imbecile. I don't know how good he is in the woods, and I don't know if he can find his ass with both hands and a flashlight. But the one thing I do know is…he ain't no game warden! And neither am I."

Later that day I have an opportunity to talk to Dave.

"I have never spent much time with bear guides," I tell him, "but I hope this guy is not a representative sample of the industry."

"No," says Dave. "We have some good guides, but Murphy sure as hell isn't one of them. Eight clients with him and only one other guide."

"I don't believe he could find a bear if it bit him in the ass."

Dave laughs. "The worst part of it is, these guys have all been here before—and they keep coming back! I don't know about the Cosa Nostra over there, but Don and Brad have been here three times before."

I tell Dave how I'd had it out with Murphy earlier that

morning and told him how we weren't fucking game wardens.

"How did that go?"

"In his mind, between me being a liar or crazy, he is definitely leaning toward crazy. I tell Dave that he's doing fine but that his gun is not legal in Massachusetts, where he's supposed to live. "Just a heads up," I say. "Tell them your brother hunts a lot in Maine, and that he loaned it to you because he knew you didn't have a good bear gun. Either that or tell them you bought it at a gun sale or won it in a raffle and brought it because you knew could use it up here. It's your story. Tell 'em whatever you want. Just make sure you tell it the same way every time."

We spend that morning and every other morning chasing ghost bears and retrieving dogs. Then, late one morning, Dave and I are standing on a dirt road waiting to hear or see any sign of the dogs that were on the run again.

"Look over here," I say, bending over a mostly dried up puddle. When Dave looks down, I place the heel of my hand in the soft dirt, lean over my straight arm, and make an impression in the dirt. Then, with my index finger, I make five evenly spaced impressions slightly above my heel.

"Look!" says Dave, feigning enthusiasm. "A bear track!"

When Murphy finally comes around to retrieve us, we show him the "bear" track we'd found. He immediately calls the other six clients over to the smoking hot trail to announce the presence of what is "at least a 300-pound male bruin" that his dogs will soon tree. He turns the hounds loose and they joyously bound into the surrounding trees and brush, happy to be out of their boxes again.

Dave, shaking his head and trying to suppress a smile, leans into me and says, "You are an asshole."

//////////////////////////////

Later that week Murphy has somewhere else to be, so he tells the New York and Jersey boys to head to their tree stands until evening. Although it's deer archery season in Maine, the Gotti gang are loaded for bear as they march out into the Maine wilderness with a selection of Heckler & Koch firearms. I see one American gun, an AR-15; two HK417s, and what I think is an H&K MP5. Semi-automatic weapons are legal for hunting in Maine, but again, this is archery season.

Neither Dave nor I have an archery deer tag, so Murphy sends us over to patch of timbered woods to hunt partridge. Only, when he says it, he leaves out the R sound. "Pahtridge."

We aren't very far from camp and can hear the ruckus of the hounds. I yelp, bay, and howl like a hound in full cry. After a minute Dave joins me on my imaginary bear hunt, and we take it up and over the next hill.

Anytime I'm out on a job, I try to remember the train-tracks, power lines, and gas lines. Whenever I'm riding around with subjects, I always make specific note of power lines or gas rights-of-ways, since they pretty much always run in a straight line for miles. If you can't tell where you are when something notable occurs, you can always use landmarks to figure it out. Your testimony will always carry more weight if you can positively point out where you were when the crime—well, the "alleged" crime—occurred. Always be prepared.

Back during my second year in uniform, I was in the Adams County Court of Common Pleas seated on the witness stand testifying on the forensics of estimating the time of death for white-tailed deer. Months earlier the local volunteer fire company had been responding to a house fire and uncovered four deer hides and heads. It was late March, and the last time you could lawfully take a deer was three months prior. Judging by the condition of the heads and hides, these four deer were killed no more than three to four weeks earlier. A little simple math should tell you there is no way these deer could have been killed back in deer season. I was being cross examined by defense counsel.

"Would the condition of the deer depend on the ambient temperature?"

"Yes," I replied. "That is correct, sir."

"Correct me if I am wrong, Officer Dubaich, but that would mean the deer parts would look fresher the lower the temperature was in the area where they were stored. The less degeneration that occurs would make the parts appear to be newer, more recently harvested."

"Again, correct."

"And, conversely, if the parts were kept at a higher ambient temperature, the tissues would degrade more quickly and appear to have been harvested at a later time."

"Yes, Counselor."

"Just to make it clear in my mind. If the weather had been warmer, your calculations could suggest the hides and heads may have come from deer harvested at least four months prior, well within the time frame in which white-tailed deer could and were legally harvested."

"Yes, sir, that is possible."

"Is it, now? No further questions, Your Honor." After that the defense counsel stopped and turned back. "Just one final question, Officer Dubaich, if it pleases the court."

"One final question," the judge growled, "but the court

is *not* pleased."

"Officer Dubaich, would you happen to know the low and high temperature for the ninety days prior the time you first harassed my client in this manner?"

"In this manner?"

"Please."

"As a matter of fact, Counsel, if it pleases the Court, I would like to submit Commonwealth exhibit one: the meteorological data for the periods October one, 1986, through March 30, 1987, from the National Weather service station at the Gettysburg Regional Airport in, of course, Gettysburg, Pennsylvania." I then showed it to the defense attorney and asked the judge if I could approach the bench.

The judge smiled and said, "By all means."

"Thank you, Your Honor. The Commonwealth rests."

"Hey, Mike," says Jimmy DeMarco. "Let's you and me take a walk." It's dark out and we just finished dinner. "I wanted to stand outside and smoke," he says, "but the goddamned dogs will start barking. You and Ryan are the only ones who can shut them up."

"My gift to the world," I reply, following him outside.

DeMarco smiles and lights up a smoke. "I've known Ryan for years now and he's a little paranoid since that whole Operation Smoky thing the Feds pulled off. Now he thinks everybody he sees is a game warden."

"No shit."

"Yeah. He told me about the talk you and he had in the truck."

"Oh, yeah? Well, I'll tell ya, I was pissed."

"Yeah, he said you were. Like I said, I've known Ryan for years. He and my Pop, God rest his soul, use to hunt together."

As we walk along, I glance over, and for the first time I notice DeMarco is wearing a shoulder holster. The gun inside looks like a Glock. I prefer not to find out if I'm correct.

"I appreciate you opting out of the short-straw draw," he says. "I've been telling Ryan to forget about it. If you were a warden, you could not find balls big enough to come back up here. Even if you weren't lying, you were going to face an angry bunch of guys who may not give you a fair trial, so to speak." He smiles. "I mean, you know what happened to all of those witches up here, right? We could just build a big bonfire, and any remaining bones would be dragged away by the animals."

DeMarco is trying to send me a clear message that I

won't misinterpret or misconstrue. He's no dummy. I'm sure he understands that, so far, no one in the camp has committed any grievous violations of the law. But we aren't done hunting yet. If he missed something, or if something were to happen that would contravene the law, he is making sure to cover all the bases just in case I am the law.

"You know what I mean?"

"Yeah, Jimmy. It ain't a pretty picture, but I get it."

Then DeMarco reaches into the left side of his jacket where the Glock is. At this point my brain is kicking into high gear. The adrenaline rush you get from stress does some amazing things to your body and mind. My entire world is contained inside a twelve-inch sphere surrounding that semi-automatic handgun.

What if he draws? Do I try to disarm him? Do I try and talk my way out of another mess? Do I hit him before he gets the gun drawn?

I have milliseconds to react as his right hand goes under his camouflaged jacket. The next thing I know his hand is coming back out toward me, and I realize I've blown it. I didn't act quickly enough. Hundreds of times I'd wondered what it felt like to get shot. Would it feel hot? Cold? How much would it hurt? Was it a burning sensation? I was about to find out.

But as his hand comes out of his jacket, it's not a

gun he's holding, it's a joint. A doob. A blunt. A fucking marijuana cigarette.

I never arrested anybody for possession of weed or paraphernalia. I'd rather they smoke a joint than drink a six-pack or a pint of liquor. As a bouncer in Dickinson, North Dakota, and during my time as an officer, I've had plenty of fights with drunken assholes, but I've never had so much as cross word with someone who was stoned. Pot smokers don't throw their empty beer cans and bottles out on game lands property. People who smoke weed don't end their lives, the lives of their passengers, and the lives of other innocent victims by getting smashed and from getting smashed. They aren't the driver who wraps his Camaro around an oak tree when he's traveling way too fast to make the turn, or the Dodge van going down the wrong side of a divided highway, whose intoxicated driver slams head-on into the car at the top of the rise in the road. No, I don't give pot smokers any trouble, as long as they don't give any trouble to me.

"You smoke?" DeMarco asks me, presenting the joint.

"Hell, Jimmy, give me the bud and a couple of Zig-Zags and I'll roll the joints for you."

That makes DeMarco smile. "Most guys like a fine Cuban cigar," he says. "Me, I prefer a nice Kona Gold. It relaxes me, helps me sleep." He lights one end of the joint and draws air through the paper tube stuffed with high-grade ganja. He takes another long pull and the end flares, glowing like a firefly in the Maine darkness before turning and handing the joint to me.

This is the drug dealer's version of the "Shoot the Deer at Night" game. The one where the poacher holds the light and you do the shooting, just to prove that you are not the law. There are a surprising number of people who have heard and unquestionably believe that if you ask an undercover cop if he or she is an enforcement officer they have to tell you, otherwise it is entrapment. That premise is, of course, ridiculous.

I'd been offered scores of drugs at numerous bars and parties, and I'd always politely declined. I never had to shoot a deer at night, and I never took any drug unless it was prescribed by my doctor.

That is, until now.

Unlike former President William Jefferson Clinton, I inhale.

When DeMarco and I reenter the dining area his three soldiers are engaged in a lively conversation with Murphy, who is talking defensively.

"I'm telling you guys," Murphy hollers, "I did not run the dogs on a hunt today!"

Sal is boisterous. "We could hear you while we were

sitting in our fucking deer stands, Ryan! Tell him, Marko."

"Sure as shit," Marko agrees. "You ran 'em up the hill where the clear-cut was and then down the other side. After that we couldn't hear you anymore."

Then Bobbie chimes in. "Who were you running dogs for, Ryan?"

Murphy remains obdurate. "I wasn't even here! You guys are all fucking numb."

"Then color me crazy, too, Ryan," says DeMarco, joining the conversation, "'cause I heard you myself."

As Murphy steadfastly proclaims his innocence, Dave just sits there, grinning like an opossum. By this point everyone is getting angry. The more they accuse Ryan, the more he denies. I nod my head toward Dave, and in stereo we begin our version of hounds hunting a bear. That stops everything. Murphy is already laughing before the New York boys realize they'd all been had.

"You fucking country boys," says Sal. "You really had us going."

"Yes, sir," says DeMarco. "And I was blaming you, Ryan. I figured you sent us out to the deer stands while you took the other four to chase a bear."

It's the first time I've seen Murphy laugh, and he seems much more relaxed. I don't know if he checked in with L.L.Bean and they backed our story, but he'd been gone for half the day. Maybe he's just happy to see that I came back from my walk with DeMarco alive. Whatever it is, he's acting more like the Ryan Murphy I'd met my first time here, relaxed and self-assured.

It's right around this time that I make one of my worst blunders of the case. All eight clients, one guide, and Murphy are still gathered in the dining/living room after another satisfying meal, when suddenly Murphy announces, "Well, Mike, every year at bear camp the cook picks one of the clients to…" then raising both hands up to make air quotes, "…'sleep with her.' And at this camp, you're the lucky man."

I immediately reply, "That ain't gonna happen, Ryan."

He looks surprised. "What? Why not?"

"Because I have a hard-and-fast rule. Not a guideline, mind you, a rule."

"And what is this rule, Mike?"

"Never sleep with a woman who weighs more than I do." Everybody has a good laugh at that. Except the cook; she didn't take kindly to it at all.

//////////////////////////////

We spend most of the day sitting around waiting while while Murphy and DeMarco search for the hounds, who romp around enjoying the sunshine. It's another spectacular fall day. We haven't so much as seen a bear, let alone tree one. The only thing we manage to track down are Murphy's dogs.

Murphy blames it on the weather. "With all of this sunshine and nice weather," he says, "it makes it hard to find or follow a fucking bear. It's hard to pick up a scent when it's been so dry." The evening is spent enjoying another good dinner, drinking beer, and telling stories. I head out to the bed in my truck hoping tomorrow will bring some activity. I'm feeling a little uneasy and can't put my finger one why.

////////////////////////////////

"You gonna sleep all day, boy," Murphy says, standing at the tailgate of my truck.

I snap awake, sweating, and disoriented. Goddamn that nightmare. It isn't always the same, and my nightmares are becoming inexorable, pernicious film snippets of sleep-deprived mistakes, stumbles, and failures. They always end with me about to die in some despicable manner.

I had fallen asleep, even started to dream, only to snap awake scrambling toward the tailgate. It wasn't the nightmare that woke me at two in the morning, though; it was the feeling that everything inside of me wanted—no, *needed*—to come out of my body. I just managed to push the cap window up and didn't bother to lower the tailgate. There simply wasn't enough time. I blew chunks, heaved, puked, hurled, called for Ralph, vomited, purged, spit up, coughed up, up-chucked, threw up. I don't know what they call it up here, boys and girls, but if they gave ribbons for it, mine would have been a genuine blue.

There is no way I can eat breakfast. I can't even take a sip of water without heaving it back up.

I am feeling a little better by around 9:30 or 10. Murphy is driving and I'm riding shotgun. It's another drop-dead gorgeous day, and I start to feel a little bit better as the day passes. I have my window down, and the warm fall air rejuvenates me. Two Walker hounds are secure in their boxes; the black-and-tans had the day off. Duchess, the old Plott, is standing in the middle of the truck bed, nose high in the air sniffing and searching for the smell of a bear.

Murphy is driving slowly down the back roads waiting for her to cry out. Meanwhile, he and I shoot the shit.

"You look a little less green now," he says. Thankfully, since me and DeMarco's little walk, there have been no more spelling and memory games.

"I learned another valuable life lesson last night," I say.

"And what would that be?"

"Never insult the cook."

Murphy laughs so hard his eyes water.

"I didn't plan on telling her," he says. "She asked me when you were coming back to her room, and I told her you weren't. She asked me why, so I told her what you said."

"Thanks a bunch," I reply.

"It was a no brainer. It's either you or my cook."

"I guess I can't fault you for that. She is a good cook." I paused, "And I guess I deserved it," I laughed.

"She was mad, all right, but I was pretty sure she wouldn't kill you."

Suddenly, Dutchess the dog, who hasn't made a sound since we got here, yowls loudly.

Murphy pulls over immediately and parks. "Mike, unclip her and put her on the ground. Don't let her jump off, though. She's too old for that. I'll release the other hounds."

As Murphy lets loose the two Walkers, they fly off the truck and head howling across the dirt road. Duchess stays on her side of the road, opposite the path of the other two hounds and disappears into the pine forest.

"We must have two different bears here!" Murphy exclaims. "That old girl has never been wrong."

Then Rawlings chimes in. "We can't chase two bears at the same time if they're not running together. You stay with the hunters, and I'll try to follow with the truck."

"We could swing around them, try to cut them off," counters Murphy. "We grab the two hounds, come back here and chase Duchess. She is on a bear for sure. Those other two meatballs could be on a different bear or trailing this bear backward."

"But we know the Walkers can tree a bear," says Rawlings. "Duchess can't tree a bear and hold it on her own anymore."

These two guides are standing along the side of this dirt road with seven hunters, not including me, discussing their plan while their dogs' howls are fading as fast an April snow. They are about to fuck this day up, just like all the previous ones.

I'm not having this shit and yell, "I'll go after Duchess! You two take the other guys and follow the Walkers."

DeMarco looks at me like I'm crazy. "You going to run out in those woods, into those mountains all by yourself? Alone?"

"It's not a big deal," I reply.

"You are fucking nuts."

John Sanders speaks up next. "I really don't think that's a good idea, Mike. You could get lost, break a leg."

"Come on, you guys," I say. "I know my way around the woods. I'll track her down, drag her back to your truck, and meet back up with the rest of the crew." I turn and look at Murphy. "This might be our last chance to kill a bear. You're the boss, Ryan. You want me to stand around with the other boys or run that old Plott down so you guys can go and get a bear?"

Murphy finally concedes. "All right. Take a good lead with you."

Finally we have a plan, and everyone scatters to gather up their guns and ammo.

Dave follows me over to Murphy's truck. "Mike, what the fuck are you doing now?"

"I am trying to get these guys a bear," I say. "He isn't doing anything illegal unless they are finding and killing bear."

"But we will be chasing the dogs. How will you find us?"

"You just stay with those gents. Don't worry about me."

Dave didn't seem too sure. "You have no idea where we're going, Mike. Hell, I have no idea where we're going."

"If I can't follow four New York City boys, two guys from Jersey, two dogs, a couple of guides, and one game warden through the Maine woods, I should turn in my badge," I say before patting Dave on the shoulder and hurrying on my way.

We've been lucky with the weather. Still no rain in sight and warm for Maine. The hardwood canopy turns into a hardwood floor, covering everything in sight, and I can easily see the disturbance in the leaves. Just as dragging your finger lightly through dry sand creates a trail, a trail of disturbed leaves is just easy to follow.

Until, that is, the hardwood turns into pine. The hoarse bawls Duchess is making are a little hard to hear as I hustle along the rainless forest floor. But when I stop for a moment, I can hear her. And I am getting closer. She is still moving away from the road but I am definitely closing the gap.

The sun has been on my left shoulder for most of the run, which means I'm heading west. I catch a couple of glimpses of Duchess and as I start downhill I have her in sight, about 200 yards in front of me. The bear she's trailing heads into some thicker, darker woods. She and I follow. The ground is starting to get a little softer by this point. It's mossy, spongy. The bear's scent is conflating with the smell of rotting wood, mold, and stale water, making it harder to follow. Duchess is struggling to keep her feet on top of the soft mounds of moss. Her paws keep punching through the moss up to her hips and shoulders, tripping her up. My feet can stay on top of the sphagnum moss blanket. It's like the difference between walking through deep snow and walking through deep snow with snowshoes.

I close our gap to around twenty-five to thirty yards. *I am finally going to catch this goddamned dog!* My celebration is premature, though, because when I press to accelerate, my boot sinks into the fleecy moss, sending me ass over teakettle into the squelchy, miry bog. I land softly yet awkwardly between two of the giant rolls of emerald green carpet. I'd been so focused on my footing and the old, grey Plott hound, I didn't realize I'd journeyed into a sphagnum mountain bog. I've heard people talk of them and seen them on shows, and now I've literally stumbled into one. Everything as far as I can see is shades of jade and emerald. If not for gravity, I wouldn't know which way is up or down. There is absolutely nothing that's not covered in verdant moss. There are no shadows, no edges, no sunlight, no dark. I can almost feel it, the way a spiderweb feels when it slides across your forehead and cheek bones and goes for your mouth or eyes as you travel a path through the woods. The atmosphere has a viridescent, fluorescent glow, and I have no sense of direction. I can't even tell which way I came in from, and I have no idea how far in I am or how far I have to go to get out.

My stomach begins to churn. Not from food poisoning but from distress mixed with anxiety. I am afraid to move in any direction for fear it will be the wrong direction and that I might never find my way back to where I started. I try to pick out a distant point to head for, to make sure I don't walk in circles. But everything in the distance seems to melt into a glaucous curtain. It's dizzying. *What if I can't find my way back? What if they have to send a search-and-rescue team to find me? What about the investigation? Dave? Will he have to tell them we are wardens? What if I've traveled farther than I thought? Am I really out in the middle of fucking nowhere?*

Now I know how they feel, the ones who panic. The ones we find a day, a week, a month later. The ones we find too late. The ones we never find at all. I never understood why we found them without shoes or jackets, lifeless and only a few steps from the trail. Now I know.

I am struggling to get myself together, I feel like the protagonist in some imaginary Stephen King novel called *The Bog*.

I start walking again. Like they say, the journey of a thousand miles begins with one step. Then I hear it—the yelping bay of good ol' Duchess! She must've sorted out the scent of the black bear she's been following.

"Thank you, old girl!" I call out. Now I know where to go. And so, the chase continues.

The sphagnum bog really takes its toll on the old Plott. After what feels like forever, we finally break out of the swamp as she chases the bear into a clearcut. That's when I get close enough to clip the lead onto her collar. "Well that's one less thing, old girl. Now we need to figure out where you led me."

Sure, we are out of the bog, but the trip through it had robbed me of my sense of direction. The most expedient method would be to backtrack our trail. But that would require going into and getting out of the green monster, and I have no intention of taking that hound or myself through there again, not without a compass.

I look up at the sky. It was clear blue when I started this quest, now it's completely overcast.

"Just what we need, girl," I tell the dog. "Fucking rain." If I can see any hint of a shadow, I can get a direction from the sun. Since we are in the northern part of the Northern Hemisphere, and knowing the sun travels east to west on the equator, the sun's arch should be to our south. I had taken notice as I headed away from the vehicles that the sun was on my left shoulder, thus I am moving west. Logic would suggest that, in order to find our way back, we must keep the sun on our right shoulder. But what little sun we have projects a shadow too weak to be seen in the brush and scrub we are standing in. So I find a smooth, flat rock, large enough to make a sundial. It's barely discernible, but I'm able to make out the faint shadow of a stick held perpendicular to the rock's face. That's enough to get me started in the right direction. To prevent walking in circles, I pick a point in the distance that's in line with the direction I'm heading. Then I'll walk to that point, select another point, and repeat.

Eventually I come upon a power line. Power lines are maintained regularly to prevent trees from growing and interfering with the lines. Since the shortest distance between two places is a straight line, power lines pretty much travel in a straight line, regardless of what they run into.

Like I said before, it makes them excellent landmarks when you are trying to figure out where the fuck you are. This particular line runs into an intersection not far from where Murphy and the others are parked. I recall that line had single poles with a crossbar near the top, and there was only a single line strung on the top of each pole,with nothing on the crossbars. And that is exactly what I'm looking at now.

Duchess looks exhausted. "Not much farther, girl," I tell her. "Hang in there." I'm not lying, either. Only a couple hundred yards away I can make out the truck and Suburban.

The day is still fairly warm by the time we get back. I don't want to lock Duchess in her box, so I tie her lead to small tree near the side of the truck, fill a bowl with water, and give her half of my PB&J, before heading off to look for the others.

When I finally track them down, the first person I see is Dave standing in the woods. "Where are the others?" I ask him.

Dave points and says, "Right down over that next hill."

"They kill a bear?"

"Yep."

"Who shot it? Don?"

"Don't know. But I heard two shots."

"You didn't see who took the shot?"

"I was back up here looking for you, Mike."

This pisses me off. "I asked you to stay with the group!"

"I was worried you were lost."

"Shit, Dave, I've been lost for years."

After that, he and I walk down to the successful hunter and the others.

When Rawlings, one of the guides, sees me, his face explodes into an ear-to-ear grin. "Boy, Mike, am I glad to see you! We thought you were lost for sure."

"Well," I say, "I tried my damnedest to prove you true. I even spent a little time in one of your sphagnum moss bogs."

"Ain't they something?"

"They ain't anything and they are everything. Old Duchess, she led me into that thing and showed me the way back out again."

"Speaking of Duchess," says Rawlings, "where is she?"

"I didn't want to put her in her box, on account of the

heat. So, I tied her lead to a small tree beside the truck and gave her a bowl of water."

Rawlings looks confused. "I just walked over there, brought the wagon back, and took Ryan over again so he could get his truck. How the hell did I miss her, twice?"

"She was probably sleeping," I reply. "She had a pretty rough day for an old lady."

Then Rawlings tells me that Murphy had to run one of his pups to the vet. "It had about a four-inch gash in its hind quarter and needed a few stitches."

"Ouch," I say. "Guess that means we're done for the day."

"You better talk to Ryan about that."

"Another half-day hunt. When's he gonna get back?"

"It only takes about an hour to get to town and back. It depends on the doc's schedule."

"Well, there's no sense in all of us standing around with our thumbs up our asses," I say. "Why don't you take your gang back to camp, and I'll wait for Ryan and show him where his hound is."

Rawlings nods in agreement. "Sounds like a plan to me. All right, fellas, load up! We're heading for camp."

When Murphy and I arrive back in camp, I feed the

dogs while he starts to skin the bear. A short time later, I join the crowd that's gathered inside Murphy's shed to witness the skinning of a bear. When I walk in, Murphy is bragging that he was the one who fired the shot that killed the bear. According to him, Don had only wounded the bear, and as it clambered down the tree it was he who drew his .357 Magnum and fired the fatal round. Why a guide would do that to a client, I have no fucking idea. Here's Don, thrilled about his first bear kill, and then this asshole takes the credit for it.

As Murphy is skinning the bear, he cuts off some large chunks of fat. The bears this time of year are loaded with fat as they prepare for hibernation. As Murphy scrapes some of the fat off the skin, his blade makes a metallic, clicking sound. Then he stops and probes the area with his knife. Giving it a little twist, he extracts a perfectly mushroomed .357 bullet.

Whenever I'm looking for a bullet for evidence, I begin by feeling under the skin on the side opposite the entrance wound. Bear and deer have a tough, elastic hide. The bullet fired from a gun can easily drill through the skin going in, but a lot of energy is transferred to the flesh and bones as it enters and continues through the animal. It rarely has enough steam to explode through the skin on the other side, since the hide stretches and pulls away from the body. More often than not, the bullet uses all of its energy before it can break through skin and remains trapped beneath.

"That is my bullet," Murphy declares. ".357 Magnum. Went right through the heart. Told you I killed that bear!"

Murphy hands the bullet to one of his fans so they can all admire it and pass it on down. I make sure I'm the last in line. Sal hands it to me. Now I need a distraction, so I squat down, pick up a chunk of bear fat with my right hand, and with my left drop the slug into the lower lefthand pocket of my vest. Then I put both hands in the bear fat, bring my hands to my leather boots, and start to rub the bear fat all over my boots.

"What in the holy name of Jesus, Mary, and Joseph are you doing?" says Sal.

"Tell them what I am doing, Ryan."

"He's waterproofing his boots," Murphy replies.

"Waterproofing his fucking boots?" Sal echoes.

"Don't you guys have fucking stores back home?" adds Marko.

That brings down the house, and everybody immediately forgets about the bullet, at least for the moment.

The last night passes without incident, and I pass on supper. Fool me once.

The next morning is still warm, but rain is coming in, and it feels more like fall. We all pack our shit and go our own ways.

As I drive south, I say to Dave, "Boy, that Murphy is some kind of dickhead for bragging about killing Don's bear. D'you see the look on his face?"

"Yeah, I talked with him about it," Dave replies. "He said it didn't matter. He was an old man who wouldn't get many chances at a bear. There's not much we can do about it anyway. We can't prove Ryan shot the bear."

A smile grows on my face as I reach into my vest pocket, pull out the slug, and toss it into Dave's lap.

///////////////////////////

I get back to Harrisburg late that night and sleep at the Island. Woj arrives in the morning.

"You've been busy," he says to me. He takes a quick look around the room revealing an archery arrow release, a box of broad heads, a radar detector, and, topping it off, a blue phase wild turkey with the fatal crossbow bolt still stuck in its breast. "Rossi called last Wednesday," he continues. "He said he had some stuff for us, so I took a drive up there the next day. I bought the broad heads, the release, and the radar detector. Then he gave me the fucking turkey."

"Nice work," I say. "You want some help logging in the evidence?"

"Same ol' Mike," he replies, smiling. "No, I carried the load while you two were up there in vacationland."

Woj and I are still sitting in the office chatting a little while later when the phone rings. I pick it up. "Hello?"

"Mr. Dubaich, sir?" The sound of Fred Merluzzi's voice always brought a smile to my face.

"Cut the crap, Freddy. What do you want?"

"We got a big problem, Mike."

"Wrongo, my friend. When *you* have a problem, *you* have a problem. *We* don't have a problem.

"Why youuuu cocka-roach!"

That makes me laugh. "OK, Freddy, what can I do you for?"

"Norman Silver." Freddy mentions one of the guys who sold me deer at Rossi's.

"Junior or three sticks?"

"Junior. Norman Jr. has gotten his ass in another drug-dealing situation."

"Go on," I say.

"Local PD recently came to me. They say Norman has information about two guys from out of town who are buying deer."

"Why, that little prick! No honor among thieves."

"He is willing to trade this information for consideration in his case."

"OK."

"OK? Mike, you guys are fucked. I can't tell him no. The local PD and the DA agreed to play let's make a deal."

"So?"

"Sew buttons! PD is going to get your names and give that information to me, and then they'll start asking questions about how the case is going. They need to know if Silver's information is good before the DA gives him a break. Silver will wonder why nothing was done with his credible information, and PD is gonna wonder why I am just letting you two ride all over my district buying deer."

"Easy, Fred," I say. "Take a deep breath. When life gives you a bunch of shit, plant a garden."

"What the fuck is that supposed to mean?"

"Use your imagination. We can make this work to our advantage."

"I'm listening."

"You give Norman a deer to sell to us. Norman goes to Rossi and says he has another deer to sell. Rossi calls us to come and get the deer. Woj and I go to Norman's to buy deer. We buy the deer. Norman gives you the money we paid him for the deer. That covers your ass. Norman gets to play SI and gets a much-deserved break. You maintain your rock-solid, law-enforcement stature. Local PD can spread the story of the two guys buying deer. Woj and I get another star on our these-guys-are-really-assholes chart. And we get our money back after prosecution, too."

PART IV

MAKIN' DEALS

PART IV: MAKIN' DEALS

It's another cold, December day, and Mike Wojtecki is at the helm as we back into the driveway of one Norman Silver Jr. The garage door slowly rattles its way up, revealing Norman dressed to the nines in his scuffed, black leather jacket. Woj parks the truck and we climb out and head into the garage. On the floor in front of us is a large blue tarp covering something. *What do you have for us today, Norman?* He pulls back the tarp exposing a large, antlerless doe lying dead on the oil-and-paint-stained concrete floor.

"Big doe," Woj says. "How much you want for her?"

"A hundred dollars," replies Norman.

"She is a big doe," I say, "but she ain't no hundred-dollars big. I'll give you seventy-five."

Norman jumps at my offer. "Deal."

Woj leans in and says to me under his breath, "He would have gone for fifty."

I step back and allow Wojtecki and Norman to load the deer. I am wearing the jacket cam and I want to capture the moment with the best possible angle, making appropriate use of ambient light. After they toss the doe into the bed of Woj's truck, Norman walks to the other side of the garage, reaches into a plastic garbage bag, and pulls out the head and hide of a "button buck," i.e., a male deer in its first year. The buttons are the two pedicles where the antlers will sprout from the following spring, when the buck becomes sexually mature. According to Pennsylvania hunting regulations, an antlered deer must have at least one antler that's three inches or more in length. So while a button buck is a buck, it is, by legal definition, an antlerless deer. Antlerless deer can only be lawfully taken during a specific season, which is still three weeks away. Norman Silver Jr. is unwittingly presenting evidence of a crime we knew nothing about.

"Can you guys get rid of this for me?" he asks us as we are turning to leave.

We both stop, and I tell Woj I'll take care of this one as he climbs back in the truck and starts the engine.

"No problem, Norman," I say. "We can take care of that for you."

He hands me the head and hide, which I roll into a giant burrito with a deer-head center. Sometimes you gotta laugh. If I was after this guy in uniform, it would've taken me hours of patrol, an affidavit of probable cause, acquiring search warrants, serving the search warrants, and hours and hours of inventory receipts, and signatures to get that head and hide. If you're a special investigator, however, they take it out and hand it right to you. Norman Silver Jr. just added at least three more counts to his growing list of offenses. He just handed me all of the evidence I would need to convict him.

I rejoin Woj in the cab of his truck. I know that Norman could never remember our license plate number without writing it down. And that's exactly what I see him do. I turn the big door mirror away from the truck, which doesn't do much for Woj, but now I have a good, clear look at Norman. I watch as he pulls a pen out of his pants and takes the cap off. And just as Woj is about to pull out, Norman starts to write the plate number on the palm of his left hand.

"Hold up a minute, Woj," I say. "I gotta see something." I step out of the truck and when Norman sees me coming, I think he's going to run. He's placed his left hand straight down his leg, with his palm against his thigh. "Whatcha writing down, Norman, your grocery list?"

At this point he's rubbing his hand as hard as possible, trying to get rid of the numbers and letters he inked onto his palm. I look down at his hand, then down at the license plate, shake my head and walk back to the door I'd left ajar.

Then I take ahold of the door and say, "Don't forget the milk and bread!" It's always a rewarding feeling for an undercover officer when the bad guys think *you're* the bad guys.

//////////////////////////////

It takes a few days for us to catch up with Officer Fred Merluzzi. I need to know what Silver Jr. told him after he'd sold us the deer. I want to know where his head is, so we can avoid any other potential problems.

"How did it go with Silver the other day, Freddy?" I ask him, and then, "Scratch that. How much did he say we paid him?"

"He said fifty dollars," says Freddy. "He wouldn't lie to me. Said he had to go back inside and change his pants. He said the big guy looked like the was going to kill him when he, aka, you, jumped out of the truck and walked back to him."

"You can tell yourself he wouldn't lie," I say, "but he would, and he did. I handed him *seventy-five* American dollars."

"Son of a bitch."

"Don't worry about it, Freddy. We'll get that back and then some."

"What makes you say that?"

"I'll lay odds that Mr. Silver didn't say a word about a head and hide from a button buck he asked us to get rid of for him. That's one charge. Then you have the theft-by-deception charge for the twenty-five bucks he shorted you."

////////////////////////////

If you believe all of the hyperbole, it's the coldest mother-murdering December day ever. Rossi, Woj, and I are walking through a mix of golden rod, foxtail, and autumn olive. I'm in the middle, with Rossi to my left and Woj to my right. We are trying to push deer to three of Rossi's buddies, who are waiting at our destination in the hopes we can chase some deer their way. In deer hunter lingo, we're putting on a "drive" or "driving deer."

Suddenly two doe blast out of the brush and are now running the wrong way straight toward me. Neither Woj nor I have killed any wildlife up to this point, and the last thing I want to do is shoot a fucking deer out in this cold and wind. My nose, fingers, and toes are ice cubes as I watch the two cervids bound toward me.

But then both deer stop broad side, not thirty yards in front of me. I can't shoot and miss at this range. Nobody is going to buy that story. Even Rossi could hit them from this distance. I look to my left and there stands Rossi, looking my way, rifle *not* raised. He is waiting for me to shoot. I choose one and bring the gun up, still hoping they will bolt and give me a reason to say "aw-shucks." Neither deer budges, however, so I center on the heart of the smaller one. At least I can make it a clean kill. I click off the safety and gently squeeze and keep on squeezing the trigger, but nothing happens. I check the safety and click it on and off, but the gun still doesn't fire. I look at the action and notice that the bolt still is back in the fire position.

By this point the deer and Rossi have seen enough. And as the deer dashes away into the safety of the woods, over the wind I hear Rossi scream, "SHOOT! SHOOT! SHOOT THOSE FUCKING DEER!"

"I am trying to shoot the fucking deer, Petey!" I yell. "My gun won't fire—it's jammed up!"

"OK," says Rossi, as he watches the deer vanish into the brush. "I know there are more deer out there. Let's stay in line, cross the airport road, and keep on pushing them straight through."

My fingers are icicles from carrying the ice block that is my rifle. The gun is dead weight to me now, so I sling it over my shoulder until we get to the road, where the change in footing gives me a reason to bring the rifle back down to the safe-carry position, something I learned at my hunter safety class almost thirty years prior.

I'm carrying my rifle waist high, with the barrel and muzzle angled down to the ground, fingers nowhere near the trigger, when all of a sudden the gun explodes in my hands, sending the 180-grain, boat-tailed bullets skipping off to my left at 2,800 feet per second and with 2,913 foot-pounds of pressure. I hear the bullet skip off the blacktop road—the road Rossi is standing on.

Holy Christ, I just fucking shot Rossi!

Turns out it was a frozen firing pin. It could have been water, soda pop, milk, juice—anything but beer; I never drink and shoot. Whatever it was, some type of liquid had frozen so tight that it kept the firing pin from springing forward and striking the primer. The minuscule amount of heat the rifle absorbed through my gloves was enough to free the firing pin, finally allowing it to strike the primer and fire the rifle.

Luckily, I just barely miss Rossi. Instead, it strikes a three-inch piece of galvanized pipe that attaches the sliding gate to the fence surrounding the airport protecting aircraft, pilots, and passengers from people like us.

We have a group of ten guys and plan to spend the

morning conducting deer drives in and around the Beltsville State Forest. Woj and I have both driven our trucks on this fine day. It makes everything run a little smoother when you have to transport two groups of five for a deer drive. One way to conduct a deer drive is to drop off some of the hunters in the party to spread apart in a straight line. Then you take the other hunters a quarter mile to a half mile up the road, spread them out in a straight line parallel to the first one, and have them walk toward each other. Now where have we seen this before? I don't know… Gettysburg. Antietam. Hundreds of other battlefields. Except these guys use high-power repeating rifles, not single-shot muskets.

You can see why deer-drive days are taxing days for Woj and me. In this motley crew, we have guys on revocation, men carrying their wife's license, guys with extra tags, guys with no tags, and two guys who shouldn't even be carrying a firearm. But despite their best effort and ours, no deer will fall to their guns this day.

Rossi is riding with me on our way back from Beltzville to his house, when he tells me he has to take a shit.

"Congratulations," I reply.

"C'mon, Mike, I really need to go. That hotel down on the left, pull in there."

"I seriously doubt they have a public restroom, Petey."

"That doesn't matter. My brother owns the hotel. Drive around back."

The building is a split-level, with one story up front and two in the back. Rossi points to a spot alongside a sedan that's parked head-in and facing a row of rooms and doors.

"I hope Sal is home," Rossi grunts, "because I really have to shit."

Sal Pietre is number two (no pun intended) at Pizza Romo. He's the manager you go to when Rossi is not around. Rossi tries the door and it's unlocked. He enters quickly, unannounced. From outside I can hear Peitre and Rossi vociferously discussing each other's legitimacy of birth.

Ever since Rossi told me he had three more deer for Woj and me back at his house, I've been trying to find myself alone with enough time to power up the camera I'd installed in the brake light on the door of the truck, as well as the GVU5 Hi-8 recorder that's located behind the bench seat I presently occupy. My truck doesn't have an extended cab, just one bench seat with the kind of back which hinges forward providing a little space to store some tools. I needed enough time to jump out of the truck, access the recorder behind my seat, plug in the camera, power up the recorder, and get back in truck. Normally, I would have all of this done in advance. But I didn't think I'd need the cameras. Upon being informed that Rossi had three more deer to sell, plans changed. Wojtecki and I now have to initiate, employ, and implement our recovery plan. My part of the plan is to stop between Beltzville and Rossi's house and, at my leisure, prepare my truck to properly capture the alleged crimes.

Originally, the plan is to have Rossi ride out with Sal Pietre. It only stands to reason that Pietre will take him back home. Pietre has other commitments, though, and can't take Rossi on the return home. So instead, Rossi jumps into my truck, all but eliminating any opportunity to set up the camera. Until now, that is.

I plug the camera into the recorder and hit the power button, but all the machine does is blink the little power-on light three times and go back to black. *What the fuck does that mean*? I don't have any idea how long it will take Rossi to take a shit, but I know how long it takes to read an instruction manual. Even if I had it with me, it would take too long. My best guess is a dead battery. I decide that my chance is over. No power, no recorder. No recorder, no tape. No tape, no irrefutable evidence.

Just then I spot the cigarette plug power accessory lying under the receiver. This particular camera model is capable of running on the twelve-volt power supply in an automobile. You plug one end into the cigarette lighter charger, the other into the recorder, and you're in business.

I don't know how long Rossi has been in there at this point, but it seems like a helluva long time. Problem is, the power socket is on the bottom of the dashboard facing me, directly above the transmission hump that's standard in every vehicle. The only solution is to run the power cord under the seat to the front firewall and then up to the power plug. Unfortunately, then the power cord is clearly out in the open. I am hoping Rossi doesn't see it, and I'm preparing a story just in case he does.

Looking up I see that he's out of the bathroom and is walking back towards my truck with Pietre. I have to get it done—now! Luckily they talk long enough that I am able to get the power cord plugged in on both ends. But as I sit there looking down on it, I realize there's no way he can miss it. It looks like circles on a zebra. This is a big mistake.

You don't need to film this transaction, I think. *You already have plenty of footage of these characters. He will see that when he opens the fucking truck door! He won't even have to get in the truck, and you'll be busted! You never should've tried this in the first place, stupid!*

Rossi and Pietre are now standing in the threshold of the door speaking Italian. I can still easily pull it out and stuff it back under the seat. Just then, with a few final insults, their conversation abruptly ends. Pietre, having heard enough from his boss, steps back into his room and shuts the door.

Rossi returns to the passenger seat in my truck, and as the door swings closed he says, "Fucking Sal. He is supposed to be working this morning." He looks like he has something else to say until he notices the new wire on the floor running between the seat and the dashboard. He's staring at it like a robin eyes a worm. Meanwhile, I'm wracking my brain for a plausible story. But, amazingly, Rossi never says a word. Guess he decides it isn't anything he needs to know about. He picks up right where his train of thought got derailed. "He said he forgot I wanted to go hunting today. I told him he would forget his own ass if it wasn't attached to him. The dumb fuck."

By the time we get back to Rossi's house, Woj is already there. "You boys get lost?"

"No" I reply. "Petey had to take a shit."

Rossi tells me to drive over to the corncrib and back up to it, which I do. Woj pulls in beside me head-first so we can use his headlights to see what we're doing.

Daylight yields to darkness early this time of year, and it's almost pitch black as we load three deer into my truck. I hand Rossi three fifty-dollar bills. I have another case I'm working on that I can use three deer for, so I head for that while Wojtecki drives back to The Island.

A few weeks later, Wojtecki and I slide in through the back service entrance of Pizza Romo, walk straight down the hallway, and make the next right into Rossi's office. His office has two doors: the one we just used and another in the middle of the wall in the back of the pizza shop, which is also the front wall of his office. Rossi's desk is situated so that, while seated, he can see everywhere through the kitchen and into the pizza shop. In the far corner are stacks of police scanners, radar detectors, VCRs, cassette decks, and stereo receivers. All brand new and still in the box. As he walks into his office, Rossi is yelling something over his shoulder to Pietre, who makes a show out of wiping off his hands and throwing the towel on the counter.

"Where the fuck have you guys been?" he turns and says to us. "I haven't seen you in a month."

I smile. "You bragging or complaining?"

"Both." Rossi sounds wounded, hurt, and angry.

"What's up, Petey?" Woj breaks in. "You look like you're mad at the world."

"That fucking Sal."

"Sal?" I say. "Which Sal?"

"You know…Sal. Sal Pietre. He comes to me on his knees last night, begging me not to kill him."

Woj and I are as quiet as a man's last breath.

Rossi continues, "That mother-fucking cocksucker is

wearing a wire for the ATF and the FBI."

At this point Woj is on one side of the room, examining the new supply of electronic equipment stacked there. I am leaning against the wall opposite of him. Rossi is between us talking and looking at me as he walks to his desk.

"That rat bastard," says the man who is wearing a wire for the first time—me. I see Woj's eyes fall from mine and down at my camouflage cargo pants. That's where I've chosen to secure the recorder and microphone connected by three feet of comm line. I pray that none of it is showing. I begin to feel a little more secure when I don't see Woj displaying any obvious sign of alarm.

The recorder is a Pearlcorder System 2000. Back then it was a commonly used dictation machine about the size of a pack of those long, skinny cigarettes. I am wearing what is known in the business as a *hard wire*, which consists of a recorder and an attached microphone. There are no transmitters, no receiver. One disadvantage of the hard wire is the amount of recording time. The tapes I'm using are the one-twenties, with sixty minutes a side. (Remember, it was before digital.) Every sixty minutes you have to flip the tape over to record the next sixty minutes, which requires the wearer to keep the recorder some place readily accessible. My cargo pants have one extra pocket with a button-down flap on each leg. I have the recorder in the pocket on my right thigh.

I'd fished the microphone up through the pocket under the pants to the belt line, through the belt line, into the back of one of those multi-tool carry holsters. I have a pair of gloves stuffed into the pocket with the recorder, along with a knife in the pocket on the opposite leg to balance the way the pants hang. From there I positioned the microphone in the gap between the tool and the leather flap that buttons down to secure the tool. There was nowhere else to put the recorder. It had to be on my body somewhere and I wanted to avoid the old TV/movie standard of attaching the main wire to your chest or back. I can drop my drawers if I have to and you wouldn't see a thing. (Shut up, Woj.)

Of course, this all means nothing if they simply pat me down or scan me. There are many types of wire detection devices out there. Most work like scanners, searching the surroundings for any electronic signal, exactly like your car radio searches for a radio signal. More expensive versions can detect the slightest whisper of the signal that occurs when spoken words are captured on cassette or reel-to-reel tape. If Rossi gets cautious or paranoid, there would be nowhere to hide the recorder to prevent them from discovering it.

Rossi is pacing back and forth in the small room.

"Can you believe that?" he says. "In my house. My shop. My mother-fucking office! Right fucking here, where you fucking guys are fucking standing—a goddamn wire!"

I feel like it's time for a change in topics. "Hey, Petey," I begin, "looks like some of our stuff came in."

"That is not all yours," he replies, cooling down. "But yours is in there. And I got a brand-new snowblower for you out in the garage."

"A snowblower?" I say, "How much you want for that?"

"I was thinking four-fifty but wait till you see it. It's brand new, shiny red."

When we get out to the garage, the snowblower is exactly as Rossi described it. A Troy Bilt, to be exact.

"What'd you say you were you asking for this?" I ask again.

"Four-fifty."

What else can I say? "Sold!"

After we load the snowblower and return to the pizza shop we pay $40 more for a home security system. Woj and I also decide to purchase a police scanner for $150. The irony of it all, having Rossi worried about Pietre's wire at the same time he's selling me stolen goods while I'm wearing one, is just too good to pass up.

Wojtecki and I are in Jim's office hours before the rest of the building is open for business. We need the early start. We have a long day ahead of us.

When I sit down in front of the boss, he looks at me and says, "You look like shit."

"Thanks for the pep talk, coach. What's the game plan?"

"How is that wiretap running?"

"Ours is doing fine, but you better let your friends at the ATF and FBI know that Sal Pietre came to Rossi on his knees, begging for his life. I would call that wire compromised."

Jim turns to Woj. "How about you, Mongo? Was your recorder on?

"Yes, sir," Woj replies. "I think tomorrow is your last deal with Rossi," Jim continues. "You guys have built a hell of a case up there, but how long is that lemon worth the squeeze?"

"We could keep it going," says Woj, "but it's just going to be more of the same thing."

"Same assholes, same shit, different days," I add.

"I think your pal Rossi was the pivot man in this circle jerk, and there's no one else we can get that isn't already connected."

"Well," I say, "if we keep the case open, we know Rossi is going to keep hammering himself and racking up the charges. Then some defense attorney is going to pick up that hammer and bludgeon us for carrying it on so long."

"You guys are buying the big, green four-wheeler tomorrow, right?"

"Yeah," I say. "That, some stereo equipment, and maybe a chainsaw, slightly used."

"After tomorrow, you boys are done with that case," Jim tells us. "You've been pushing your luck up there anyway. It's been going on now for five years. Now you're wearing that wire and walking around with all that cash...I should've had you backed up when he made his first offer." Then he perks up, "I could head up there tonight and cover you in the parking lot if you'd like. I'll sit out there with my AR-15."

"Thanks, boss," I say, "but we didn't need backup then, and we won't be needing it tomorrow either."

He regards me seriously. "Well, you just make damn sure you call me as soon as you get out. If you don't, I will have your asses. I'll be home all night tomorrow. You know the number."

When we get outside, the sun is the top half of an orange and climbing.

"What the fuck was that?" Woj says, laughing.

"I think he's been watching too many shows on the Hallmark Channel," I say. "If he got within sight of the mall, they would make him in two seconds.

Jim's an excellent officer, one of the best. He's no undercover officer but I've always given him credit for trying.

The first time Jim tried to help out with SI training was in Philadelphia, aka "The City of Brotherly Love." At the time we had two new additions to the unit: Rich, a rookie out of the last class, and Chris, an officer with three years in uniform under his belt. I had a couple of court dates in neighboring counties, and Jim tried to make as many of our Court of Common Pleas cases as possible. The new guys were in listen-and-learn mode.

One of my first covers in Philly was an exotic meats and seafood business. The game commission had a refrigeration unit that was permanently mounted on a red, one-ton diesel pickup truck. I would take orders for striped bass, crabs, and shrimp, travel to Philly or Baltimore to fill my orders, and then return to the bars, restaurants, and pubs to sell them.

Jim and I arrived at the fish market around 6 a.m., and it was the wrong time to be there. The place was really hoppin'. There were a few vendors still open to pick up stragglers when we walked up the concrete steps serving the loading dock, where the majority of the vendors display their wares. Jim walked straight, and I took a hard left.

Chris asked me where I was going. I told him as far away from Jim as possible. He gave me questioning look, so I stopped where we could see Jim and, more importantly, could still hear him. I had witnessed the subtle methods Jim employed when interviewing subjects who are not supposed to know they are being interviewed. Now it was time for Chris to be educated. And it didn't take long.

Jim, wearing a Lewes Yacht Club baseball cap and tinted Ray-Ban aviator sunglasses, walked with purpose over to a vendor displaying white striped bass (aka, striper) to "solicit information" on the fish. Jim must've figured the vendor was psychic or something because, after only a few questions, the vendor looked at him and straight up asked if he was a game warden.

Another time I was in East Stroudsburg, Pa., also for a court appearance. Jim came up, drawn in part by the millions of American shad that swim north up the Delaware River to spawn each spring.

"You ever been shad fishing, Mikey?"

"Nope."

"You have your fishing gear with you?

I nodded.

"Good," he replied. "Get your rod and reel and meet me at my car. I'll take you down to the river."

"Let's take my truck instead."

"What's wrong with my car?" Jim drove a silver, four-door Plymouth Fury III sedan, with moon hubcaps and the long antenna.

"It looks like a fucking cop car, Jim."

He frowns. "You've been out here too long, Mikey That is not a 'cop car.'"

"C'mon, Jim, I still have a couple of good cases near here. I can't be seen riding around in that thing."

"Whatever," he says. "You've been watching too much TV."

We're sitting there for a minute when (I swear), a man steps out the front door of the hotel and walks quickly toward us.

"Wonder what this guy wants," Jim says.

"Boy," the unknown man said, "you guys sure got here fast. We only called a couple of minutes ago."

"We are not the police!" Jim snaps, looking up at the confused man who turns and walks away. Then Jim turns, looks at me, and with all honesty and sincerity says, "Now why in the world would that guy think we we're cops?"

///////////////////////////////

Wojtecki and I make the two-hour drive to Leighton, Pa., as "Mike Walker" and "Mike Duncan" for the last time. The boss is right—it's time to pull the plug on this operation. The wiretap is a really tedious and time-consuming procedure, and it isn't telling us anything we don't already know.

I am wired for sound again. Like the cameras I've been wearing for a couple of years at this point, you just gotta get used to it. The microphone, we discover, is extremely sensitive. Just like you see in the movies any mechanical noise will really override the human voice. We have to be really careful with the placement of the microphone so there's no rustle of clothing or scratching noise.

Rossi would have to be dead to constrain his dialog to one sixty-minute side of a micro-cassette tape. I have to flip it over during our meeting, and another sixty minutes is barely enough. Fortunately, the pizza shop has one of those one single-option restrooms with a door you can lock, giving me all the privacy I need to flip the tape and reinstall the recorder.

We usually arrive around lunch time but Rossi wants us to wait till around five. It will be dark soon, he says, and he doesn't want to haul that big four wheeler around too much in the daylight. "Things are getting hot," he tells us.

We enter in our usual way, through the backdoor service hallway, and when I open the outside door, the smell of gasoline hits me. Usually the only thing in Rossi's pizza shop that's dirty is him; the place is always spotless. The source of the fuel smell is a Stihl 034 AV chainsaw, which is sitting on the concrete floor against the left side wall. Twenty-four-inch bar, made for big timber. Good saw. I have the same one at home. Beside it is one of those heavy, leather tool belts, the kind that lineman and tree trimmers wear. When I spot the chainsaw lying there, my mind flashes to Al Pacino in "Scarface." You know, that scene in the bathroom. I decide not to share my thoughts with Woj.

"That's a nice saw," I say as we turn into Rossi's office. He's at his desk, counting money.

Stopping counting, he looks up and says, "It's for sale."

"Hey, Petey," I say, "you ever hear the one about the Italian and the chainsaw?" I pause as he leans back in his chair and starts to grin. "Well, this Italian guy goes to a hardware store buys a chainsaw, and the salesman asks if he needs any assistance. The Italian waves the salesman off and says, 'I don't need any help. I know how to use a goddamned chainsaw.' A week later the Italian comes back to the hardware store, and his hands are all blistered and bleeding. He tells the salesman, 'This saw was supposed to make cutting wood easy, but it only made it harder!' So the salesman takes the saw, flips the switch to run, sets the choke, pulls the rope one time, and the saw fires right up.

He looks over at the Italian guy, and the Italian guy shouts, 'What's that noise!'"

"Fuck you guys," says Rossi. "Both of you! You missed the guys with the chainsaw. They left a couple of minutes ago. I wanted you to talk with them about it, 'cause I don't know shit about chainsaws. How much you think it's worth?"

"It depends on who's buying," I reply. "Doesn't look like it was used real hard. How about a hundred even?"

"You can have it for that," Rossi says. "I'll even through in the tool belt."

After that Wojtecki gives Rossi $200 for a VCR and $150 for a cassette player. By then the lights inside the makeshift mall belie the darkness outside. The sodium arch lights positioned throughout the parking lot allow Woj and I to transfer our spoils of war to my truck without incident.

Rossi tells us he has a quad he's looking to sell too, so we follow him to his house and back up the pickup to the left-side garage door. The key switch on the ATV has been punched and the ignition wires are all twisted together. Grabbing the wires from the starter, I hold them against the ignition wire until the starter cranks the motor long enough to fire up the four-stroke gasoline engine.

"You look like you've done this before," says Rossi, watching me hot-wire the engine.

"You don't want to know," I reply.

///////////////////////////

"Fuck, Woj! We were supposed to call Jim to let him know he didn't have to worry about receiving two fish wrapped in newspaper."

I look down at the clock in the instrument panel of the truck and see that it's eighteen-hundred hours. It was seventeen-thirty when we left Rossi's. We had been there for two and a half hours. Jim had probably called every law enforcement personnel in the area code. Remember, it's 1996. Personal cell phones are still unheard of, at least for state employees. I have to find a payphone if I want to make a call.

"I will be home all night," Jim had told us over the phone. "You better call me as soon as you get out of there," adding, "I am not fucking around here. You have no idea how much shit you two have stirred up. I want you out of that town!"

Apparently, in addition to Pietre's wire, Norman Silver has been working with the District Attorney by wearing a wire on Rossi, who tells us about Norman that evening, after I flip the cassette over and the entire 120 minutes of recording time expires.

Another reason law enforcement people are dubious about wire taps is that, if there are any gaps in the recording or the recorder gets turned on and off more than once, the defense attorney invariably will attack the wire's validity. They claim that any space or blank spots was the prosecution editing out conversation favoring the defendant.

I allow the phone to ring six times before hearing Jim's voice on his answering machine. "Good thing you and I aren't laying out here bleeding to death, Woj," I laugh as I climb back into my pickup. "Got his answering machine."

///////////////////////////////

I'm typing up some reports when the phone rings on my desk at The Island. It's Jim. And he's pissed. More than pissed. I allow him swear at me for a minute or so, then I ask, "Boss, do you have an answering machine?"

"Yeah," he replies, "it's downstairs."

"Have you checked your messages today?"

"Today? Well, uh…MONGO!"

EPILOGUE

EPILOGUE

When it's all said and done, we file a total of 122 charges against fifteen separate Carbon County residents, including:

- Peter "Petey" Rossi, sixty-five Game and Wildlife charges, six Crimes Code violations
- Raymond Gibson, twenty-five counts
- Sal Pietre, twelve counts federal firearms violations, served with an arrest warrant for parole violations
- Norman Silver Jr., six counts
- Norman Silver III, three counts
- Giuseppe Rossi, three counts
- Kimberly Rossi, three counts

Participating in the arrest are members of the State Police Organized Crime Strike Force and special agents of the Federal Bureau of Alcohol, Tobacco, and Firearms.

A search of Rossi's home reveals a number of handguns, hunting rifles, and assault-style weapons. Also confiscated from the residence are taxidermy mounts of state and federally protected birds and mammals including a bobcat, a great horned owl, a hawk clutching a chipmunk in its talons, and two white-tailed deer fawns. One of the game commission officers participating in the search unexpectedly found a real, solid-gold bar in Rossi's safe.

Rossi insists on a jury trial so he can be judged by a jury of his peers. Woj and I testify, and the district attorney decides not to use the tapes from the body wire. He doesn't want to give defense counsel anything to conflate the testimony that the jurors hear. They love the camera tape footage we shot of us counting out the money and handing it to Rossi. The owners of the electronic equipment, the snowblower, the quad, and the three-wheeler all identify their respective stolen property. Rossi has a friend who testifies he purchased both off-road vehicles and the snowblower from a guy he claimed was from out of town, and then sold them to Rossi. He never thought they were stolen himself, and so he never told Rossi they were stolen. He also says he cannot remember name of the man he bought the three items from.

The jury finds Rossi guilty as charged. Since he has no prior convictions, the judge sentences him to six months in prison and four years' probation.

I never hear anything about Ryan Murphy, and I never ask.

I end up seeing Sergeant Dave Malone on an episode of "North Woods Law," and I'm happy to see he was promoted.

///////////////////////////////

The man who sold me thirty-four bear gallbladders pays a fine and costs of $40,430: $20,000 in cash and $425 per month for four years, for unlawful trafficking.

Gino Lombardi ends up somewhere in the US Federal Witness Protection Program.

///////////////////////////////

Bud and Lou each plead to one count of theft, which are second counts for both of them, so they went back to prison and paid restitution to the landowners whose timber they stole. When the attorney general bowed out, we, the Pennsylvania Game Commission, didn't have the money or the personnel to set up a log yard on our own so we weren't able to take the case further..

As for good ol' Tom the poacher, I got busy working other cases since none of his crimes with me were of a commercial nature and that is the primary focus of the SI unit. Back then the charges for poaching alone were fairly minor and I had some good cases close to that area that I couldn't risk by giving up my cover to arrest him. By the time the other cases are resolved the two-year statute of limit of limitations on Tom's charges have already expired.

Jim Beard retires, and I am promoted to fill his position. In a few years, my next boss retires too, and I am again promoted. In doing so I become the youngest state director of law enforcement in the country.

//////////////////////////////

The phone on my desk is ringing and line two is flashing. Whenever possible, I always answer my own phone. I figure my assistant has more important things to do than screen my calls. So I put the phone to my ear and speak. "Law enforcement, Mike Dubaich."

The voice I hear is unmistakably that of one Peter Rossi. "Mike, this is Petey."

"What can I do for you, Mr. Rossi?"

"You gotta be kidding me with this revocation thing. The fines are bad, but they don't hurt me. It's the license, Mike. I can't hunt again till I am eighty years old!"

"That's how it is supposed to work, Petey. You were

lucky. I was pushing for a lifetime ban."

"C'mon, Mike. You know I didn't shoot those deer."

"You weren't charged for killing them. You were charged with *selling* them."

"Well, you look like you have done pretty good for yourself, thanks to me."

Now I'm pissed and trying to hold my temper. "Look, Petey, I got what I earned through hard work and honesty. You got what you earned by being a liar and a thief!" I pause for a moment and then say, "Now, Mr. Rossi, is there anything else I can do for you?"

And with that, I hear Rossi's patented response: "Fuck you guys."

ABOUT THE AUTHOR

Michael Dubaich is a former undercover special agent and master instructor for the Pennsylvania Game Commission.

A native of Aliquippa, Pa., Dubaich earned a B.S. in Fish and Wildlife Management from Montana State University in 1983. He is a 1985 graduate of the Pennsylvania Game Commission Training School. He completed his covert investigations training at the Federal Law Enforcement Training center in Glynco, Georgia, and earned his Class-A wiretap and electronic surveillance certification in 1988.

Over his 22-year career, Dubaich served as a firearms master instructor, GLOCK firearms armorer, unarmed self-defense master instructor, PR 24 police baton master instructor, Hiatt hinged handcuff master instructor, invited instructor for the Federal Law Enforcement Training Center, sworn special agent for the Pennsylvania State Attorney General, president of the North East Conservation Law Enforcement Chiefs Association, and member of the National Law Enforcement Trainers Association. He is also a wildlife artist who has shown his paintings in juried exhibitions and illustrated articles for the PGC Game News Magazine.

Dubaich was diagnosed with early onset Parkinson's disease at age of 40. Seven years later he had bilateral deep-brain stimulators implanted in an effort to reduce the symptoms.

He retired from PGC in 2007 but continues with his artistic endeavors.

Made in United States
North Haven, CT
07 March 2023